P9-AFQ-512

THE DARK SIDE OF THE HOUSE

THE DARK SIDE OF THE HOUSE

by YALE DAVID KOSKOFF, M.D.
and RICHARD GOLDHURST

The Dial Press, Inc.

New York 1968

ACKNOWLEDGMENTS

Gratitude is warmly expressed to:

Dr. Paul Yakovlev of Harvard University, renowned neuropathologist, for his detailed study of the brain of Millard Wright and for the illuminating photographs of the gross and microscopic structures.

Dr. Ralph Weaver, pathologist of the Butler Hospital, Butler, Pa., for his significant observations at autopsy.

Captain William Hanna, Chief of the Butler Barracks of the Pennsylvania State Police, who disclosed the final events in the life of Millard Wright, and Captain Louis Rosenau of the Westport, Connecticut, Police Department.

Mr. Jeremiah A. O'Mara, Chief Librarian, Western Psychiatric Institute and Clinic, School of Medicine, University of Pittsburgh, for his valued aid in searching the psychiatric literature.

Eric G. Koskoff, attorney at the Pennsylvania Bar, for his clarification of certain aspects of criminal law.

Miss Henrietta D'Alo, secretary of the Department of Research, Montefiore Hospital, Pittsburgh, for her untiring preparation of numerous preliminary manuscripts; and to Mrs. Esme Henry of Westport, who speedily typed the final draft.

Mrs. Nancy Reedy, for her devoted secretarial help.

Mr. Gerard McCauley, friend and adviser, who recognized the possibilities of the work, and E. L. Doctorow, who guided it to completion.

Mr. M. Marc Goldberg and Mr. Gerard F. McCauley, friends and advisers, who recognized the possibility of the work.

The diagram in the first photo insert is reprinted from *Psychosurgery* by Freeman and Watts, 1942. Courtesy of Charles C. Thomas, Publisher, Springfield, Illinois, and the authors.

for BETKA KOSKOFF

whose love protected the precious of the past
while creating a future of fulfillment

The clever burglar will invariably enter a house from its dark side, the side on which the moon does not shine.

—*A Practicable Manual for Detection,* 1896
New York Police Department

Let us go back to house-symbolism when in a dream we make use of the projections on houses for catching hold of, we may be reminded of a common vulgar expression for well-developed breasts: "She's got something to catch hold of." There is another popular expression in such cases, "She's got plenty of wood in front of the house," which seems to confirm our interpretation of wood as a female, maternal symbol.

—*The Complete Psychological Works of Sigmund Freud,
Introductory Lectures on Psychoanalysis.*

A NOTE ON THE SOURCES

The authors have drawn the material for this book mainly from Yale David Koskoff's many conversations with Millard Wright, as doctor and friend, and from the two detailed autobiographies that Wright prepared before and after his operation. In addition, interviews with Wright's widow and others who knew him well, with doctors at Monte-fiore Hospital involved in his case and with police officers have been helpful. However, since their attempt has been to present a continuous perspective of Millard Wright's life from beginning to end, the authors have found it necessary from time to time to recreate dialogue, to make certain psychological judgments and assess the motives of people who directly or indirectly influenced the course of Millard Wright's criminal and medical careers.

YDK

RG

Contents

Prologue   xi

    PART I   The Repeater   1
    PART II   The Penitent   89
    PART III   The Loser   163

Photograph Inserts   *facing pp. 42 and 138*

Appendixes   211

    "In Search of Decisive Judgments"
    by Yale David Koskoff
    Facsimiles of Pre-operative and Post-operative
    Writings by Millard Wright

Prologue

On the morning of September 13, 1848, Phineas Gage, a twenty-five-year-old foreman for the Rutland and Burlington Railroad in Vermont, prepared to blast a large shelf of rock. Gage, an industrious, efficient boss, much admired by his men, was also a pious and reverent churchgoer. Handling explosives, he always asked God's help. After pointing out where he wanted the holes drilled, Gage told his crew to charge the fuses.

They finished. Gage went to pack each explosive charge with a tamping iron 3 feet 7 inches in length, 1¼ inches round, weighing 13¼ pounds, a long bar tapering from 3 inches to a point ½ inch in diameter. At each hole, Gage carefully tamped dirt atop the dynamite so that the charge would split the rock-shelf laterally instead of expending itself skyward. He came to the last one. One of the workmen had forgotten to cushion the fuse with a layer of sand.

With Gage's first tap, the dynamite exploded.

Driving upward through Gage's cheekbone, straight through his skull, the tamping iron landed with a clang several yards behind him.

The bang, the yells of the workcrew, brought Dr. John Harlow from the construction shack. He raced to Gage, who, hands to cheekbone, lay on his side, kicking convulsively. Harlow heard him ask for help before turning him on his back. There was a three-inch hole in Gage's skull and a three-inch hole under his eye. The men gently lifted the hurt man in their arms and carried him to the road where they placed him in an oxcart. Harlow retrieved the tamping iron which was covered with blood and was greasy to the touch. Gage sat up and remained sitting until he reached the hotel, three-quarters of a mile away. The cart was drenched with blood.

Assisted by the crew, and by Harlow, Gage got out and, after resting on a chair on the hotel porch, walked up a long flight of stairs to his room, where Harlow began to dress the wound. He remained conscious through the whole process, although Harlow saw the hemorrhage was exhausting him. Blood kept pouring from his head. Gage was also swallowing blood, which caused vomiting every fifteen or twenty minutes. But he was able to say, "The iron entered my cheek here and went right through my head." Gage recognized Harlow and asked, "Am I hurt much?" Harlow didn't tell him death was a matter of minutes.

Harlow was surprised his patient made it through the afternoon—and evening.

For the next five days, Gage remained conscious. Then delirium from the accompanying infection set in. Harlow cut away the herniated brain tissue and drained the blood and pus. Twenty-three days after his injury, Gage sat up in his bed for four minutes and told Harlow he felt comfortable. Five days later, Gage was able to recount how long he had been in bed, knew that he had been injured by an accidental explosion, and accurately placed the time of day the dynamite went off. On the sixty-fourth day, Gage walked a half-mile to the company store, bought towels and coffee, paid for them with his usual accuracy, although the clerk noted his customer didn't care what it cost as long as he had the money. Three months after the accident, Harlow judged his patient's recovery complete.

A year later, Dr. Harlow wrote in his medical record: "General appearance good. Stands quite erect with his head inclined slightly toward the right side; his gait in walking is steady; his movements rapid and easily executed . . . There is no pain in the head but patient has a queer feeling which he is not able to describe. Applied for a situation as foreman but is undecided whether to work or travel. His contractors, who regarded him as the most efficient and capable foreman in their employ previous to his injury, considered the change in his mind so marked that they could not give him his place again. The equilibrium of balance, so to speak, between his intellectual faculties and his animal propensities seemed to have been destroyed. He is fitful, irreverent, indulging at times in the grossest profanity (which was not previously his custom), manifesting but little deference to his fellows, impatient of restraint or advice when it conflicts with his desires, at times pertinaciously obstinate yet capricious and vacillating, devising many plans for future operation which are no sooner arranged than they are abandoned in turn for others appearing more feasible. A child in his intellectual capacities but with the general passions of a strong man. Previous to his injury, although untrained in school, he possessed a well-balanced mind and was looked upon by those who knew him as a shrewd, smart business man, very energetic in executing all his plans of operation. In this regard his mind was radically changed, so that his friends and acquaintances said that he was no longer Gage."[1]

Over the next thirteen years, Phineas Gage made a living of sorts, first with Barnum's circus, then in South America where he tried to establish a coach line in Valparaiso. He died in San Francisco in May, 1861. Through the offices of the mayor, Dr. Alfred Coon, and D. B. Shattuck, the patient's brother-in-law, Harlow obtained Gage's skull. He had always kept the tamping iron. He presented both to the Warren Museum at Harvard. In medical history Gage is known as the "crowbar case." To this day, the crowbar case is not only the classic but still the definitive study of frontal lobe brain damage.

Though Harlow didn't know the word, he was one of the first doctors to assess and analyze, correctly and accurately, the results of a frontal lobotomy. His patient, Gage, had accidentally subjected himself not only to a brain operation but to psychosurgery, both of which are older than medicine itself.

In the middle of the nineteenth century, the French anthro-

[1] *Psychosurgery* by Walter Freeman and James W. Watts. Springfield, Ill.: Charles C. Thomas, 1842, p. 45. (The original was first published one hundred years ago in the Publications of the Massachusetts Medical Society. 1868, Vol. 2, pp. 237-346.)

pologist Prunière discovered at Lozère the first trephined neo-lithic skulls. A trephine is a circular saw mounted on a metal shaft used to remove disks from the skull, round buttons of bone. Trephined skulls have been unearthed from the Babylonian and Egyptian, the Greek and Roman cultures, but it was the Incas of Peru who brought trephination to a high art. Hundreds of skulls have been unearthed in the Peruvian highlands, each perfectly trephined.

Probably semicivilized and civilized man started trephining in the attempt to let out evil spirits. No doubt migraine headaches, epilepsy, or *tic douloureux* provided excuses for the witch doctor or priest to carve buttons from the skull. But somewhere along the line, it was discovered that trephination had a therapeutic effect. A neolithic or Peruvian skull with a fracture line and a trephine opening indicates the surgeon understood the relation-ship between physical injury and mental disorder. Trephining produces far less pain than most people suspect. During World War I, it was a common operation on men who had suffered head wounds.

It is by trephining the skull that the modern neurosurgeon removes the tumor or the glioma, clips an intracranial aneurism, or drains an abscess. Neurosurgery is the surgical treatment for *physical* disorders within the nervous system. Psychosurgery is the surgical treatment of *mental* disorders; the psychosurgeon relieves mental abnormalities in a nervous system anatomically normal. Without question, psychosurgery is the older of the two techniques.

Brain surgery, however, has not been the only approach to alteration of the psyche. Primitive warrior tribes castrated their prisoners of war, invariably a successful operation. Castration re-duced aggression and hostility among captives and removed a menace from the environment. Eventually it produced the first slaves.

The most successful psychosurgical technique ever developed is lobotomy, the severing of the frontal lobes by incision, just as the tamping iron severed them in Phineas Gage. Lobotomy, of course, is as destructive an attack on the individual as castration but with this difference: The psychosurgeon aims at integrating and restoring the individual to the environment, not isolating him, he aims at salvaging some of the individual's powers, not depriving him of more.

Lobotomy has had a successful though ambiguous and interrupted career. During its first wave of popularity in the early 1940's, brain surgeons and some neurologists greeted this technique enthusiastically, yet there were theologians, philosophers, psychiatrists, and other physicians who condemned it. In the Soviet Union today, the operation is proscribed.

In England, however, it is not at all uncommon. In the United States many neurosurgeons and psychiatrists rely much more on the use of drugs in treatment of psychotics, but doctors do lobotomize some whom tranquilizers cannot soothe. Lobotomies are also performed on some cancer patients suffering intractable pain. The longer the pain persists, the more it generates anxiety, keeps warning a man or woman that death is an impending fact. That anxiety can ravage the mind and body more than pain. For that is what suffering is: pain plus anxiety, pain constantly influenced by fear.

The frontal lobes have vast intertwining connections like fine telephone cables with brain areas that serve emotion. A surgeon can cut a few strands for a "narrow" lobotomy or many for a "deep" lobotomy thereby severing the "thinking" brain from the "feeling" brain. A certain internal conflict will come to an abrupt rest.

The first surgical lobotomy, deliberately performed, was undertaken by the Swiss psychiatrist G. Burckhardt over seventy-five years ago. Burckhardt was superintendent of a small mental institution. Having dealt all his professional life with the violently and critically insane, Burckhardt came to the conclusion that in patients suffering mental disorders, it was pointless to continue treating other regions of the body. As he put it, "No one changes the weather by adjusting the weather vane." To relieve insanity, the surgeon would have to find some way to treat the brain itself. Burckhardt came across the animal experiments reported by a German colleague, Dr. F. L. Goltz, and these led him to the conclusion that the treatment of different cortical regions in the brain might have variable effects on human emotion. Goltz, whose report was published in 1884, revealed that in dogs whose frontal regions had been removed there was a greater hostility and anger than in dogs whose posterior regions had been altered or excised. Burckhardt had observed that in humans the reaction was the opposite. He knew from clinical experience that patients who suffered a biological affliction in the frontal lobes were quieted and calmed as the brain tissue deteriorated. He decided that he would therefore operate on the frontal regions of the brain.

The patient Burckhardt chose was a severely disturbed schizophrenic woman, fifty years old. She had spent the last fifteen years in the asylum, forever disturbed, forever unapproachable, held in constant restraint by her attendants. She fought doctors and other patients indiscriminately, she spat and hissed hour after hour, was manifestly untidy and lacked bowel and bladder control. Inspiring her disturbed behavior was a succession of frightening hallucinations. Her perverted speech mechanisms distorted potentially normal associations within her environment.

Burckhardt reasoned that if he could remove the exciting impulses from her brain mechanism, he could transform his patient from a disturbed to a quiet dement. He operated on four consecutive occasions and cut the two frontal lobes. After each of these operations, there was a marked reduction in excited and disturbed behavior. After recuperating from the fourth operation, this woman slept late and ate well. She was more tractable and could mingle with the other patients. She still suffered hallucinations, but reacted less frenziedly to them. Nurses and doctors no longer feared her tantrums. Her bowels, which had alternated between constipation and diarrhea, became normal. Her intelligence never returned, but she was quieter and on occasion euphoric.

Burckhardt operated on five more patients, one of whom died. Of his fourth case, Burckhardt wrote: "The plainly visible result of the operation is that the patient has been altered from a disagreeable, occasionally violent patient, dangerous to his comrades and confined in a disturbed ward, into a harmless working patient inhabiting a quieter ward. Demented he remains, but the dementia has not increased; on the other hand in many respects it has decreased. I am certain that the patient suffers less from hallucinations than he did before, and those that remain, according to the patient's statement, are not so intense as before."[2]

Burckhardt published his findings in 1890–91 with the apologia, "Better a perilous remedy than none." To the recriminations which followed, to the charges that he had destroyed parts of the personality, committed an unjustified assault upon patients under his care, he replied, "My purpose could not be other than to transform a dangerous sick person into a harmless one."

Burckhardt had a practical as well as a scientific motive. Insane asylums at the turn of this century were jungles filled with tigers; one who lives with tigers must sooner or later learn to tame them. Since most of his contemporaries never lived with tigers, Burckhardt outraged them with his coldly precise reasoning. By today's standards, his operations were mutilating and crude; they endangered the language areas of the brain, which made them inapplicable in the treatment of mental disorders.

After his sixth operation, Burckhardt himself gave up further experimentation and research. Nor did he inspire any disciples. Within the decade, however, intracranial surgery became a successful technique for the removal of tumors which provoked abnormal mental symptoms, for the extirpation or coagulation of cortical foci which produced convulsions, for the relief of pain through operations on the Gasserian ganglion and its root. Yet the problem of how to treat ill or sick people whose nervous systems and brains were normal still remained.

In the summer of 1933 John F. Fulton of Yale University reactivated interest in lobotomy as a prospective surgical technique. When a research team at Johns Hopkins, studying the common cold, no longer needed some of its animals, Fulton claimed two six-year-old chimpanzees named Becky and Lucy. Assisted by Carlyle Jacobsen of Yale's Physiology Laboratory, Fulton subjected these chimps to an extensive set of behavioral tests.

Fulton found Becky loving and affectionate, Lucy cranky and quiet, and neither too bright. They could pass most of the tests

---

[2] *Ibid.*, p. 8.

but one distressed and confused them. Food was placed under one of two identical cups. A sliding panel then blocked Becky's and Lucy's view. When the panel was removed Becky and Lucy had to remember under which cup the delicacy lay. They couldn't. They couldn't even make the guess. Their failure drove them into a rage.

Deprived of their sweet, they would cry, scream, rage, urinate and defecate, shake the bars, roll on the floor, and deliver themselves to uncontrolled temper tantrums. As the daily tests went on, they developed full-fledged mental disorders.

John Fulton lobotomized both, taking out small pieces from their lobes. After the operation, Becky and Lucy still couldn't pass the test, but neither cared any longer. The lobotomy relieved their frustrational behavior and improved their conduct. The two chimpanzees stopped worrying. They continued in test situations long beyond normal patience, going through the motions of selecting this or that choice until the patience of the examiner himself was exhausted, yet they never exhibited anger, despair, or futility. "It was as if the animal had joined the happiness cult of the Elder Micheaux and placed its burdens in the Lord."[3]

John Fulton, of course, had much more advanced scientific knowledge than Burckhardt. The work of Doctors Harvey Cushing, Fedor Krause, Victor Horsley, William Macewen had taught him a great deal about the functioning of the brain. He also benefited from the work of Sigmund Freud and from the research of Sir Charles Sherrington on the integrative action of the brain as the organ of the mind and the nervous system—secrets at which Burckhardt couldn't guess. Knowing that there was a complex relationship between mind, brain, and behavior, John Fulton and his colleague Carlyle Jacobsen were able in one predictable instance to affect this relationship surgically.

At the 1935 International Neurological Congress in London, Fulton described the results of the operations on Becky and Lucy. In sum, Fulton reported that chimpanzees in whom the bilateral frontal region had been removed did not show tension, anxiety, or neurotic behavior when they made errors in conditioned responses. Among the audience sat Dr. Egas Moniz of

[3] *The Human Brain* by John Pfeiffer. New York: Pyramid Publications, 1964, p. 186.

Lisbon, Portugal. Moniz had guessed some time before that he might be able to treat psychotic patients by a surgical interruption of their frontal association pathways, but before he proceeded, he wanted empirical and clinical justification. Fulton's report gave Moniz's ideas purchase.

By November of the same year, Moniz and his neurological colleague, Almeida Lima, performed their first lobotomy. In all, they were to perform twenty.

Moniz introduced two innovations. He invented the leucotome—for several years the operation was called a leucotomy—a hollow needle which carried within it a razor-sharp wire as a cutting blade. Also, when Moniz cut one centimeter of white matter in the lobes, he did not remove it but left it free in the cavity to undergo autolysis (self-digestion).

On the eve of his first operation, Moniz was filled with a natural anxiety. Even if successful, the operation, he knew, would provoke strong controversy in medical, religious, and philosophic circles. Despite this concern, he went ahead, hoping that such discussion would serve the progress of science, and that the operation would be of use to the mentally ill.

Subjecting twenty patients to close pre-operative and post-operative observation, Moniz demonstrated conclusively that psychic functions and regions of the brain which contribute to their manifestation are in close relation to one another.

Among his patients, Moniz generally noted akinesis and loss of initiative, which seldom lasted more than two or three weeks. Half were unresponsive to their surroundings but this also disappeared in three or four days. In their early recovery phases, almost all of his patients were disoriented in place and time; and four were constantly hungry. A few collected things which belonged to others. All these symptoms were transient. Sooner or later the brain compensated, just as a heightened sense of touch will compensate for the loss of sight. Concerning memory and intelligence, Moniz concluded: "In all our operative attempts one fact presents itself with great clarity—it is that the destruction of a considerable number of connections in the two pre-frontal lobes is not accompanied by any grave repercussion on the part of the intelligence or the memory."[4]

[4] Freeman and Watts, *op. cit.*, p. 13.

Seven of his patients improved enough to make a social adjustment to work and family; seven improved to live more relaxed lives within the institution; six showed no change. None deteriorated. In all these patients, there was a noticeable blunting of personality. Moniz had induced an anatomical loss for a behavioral gain.

That gain is of supreme importance for psychotic patients. Men and women suffering mental disorders of pronounced distress are not only problems and burdens to themselves, but to their environments and to their families, to their attendants and fellow patients. Thousands of lobotomized patients have returned to normal life.

Moniz was not only a daring and imaginative, a skilled and delicate surgeon, but he was a sympathetic man, a man of many parts. Before this experiment, collaborating again with Almeida Lima, Moniz devoted himself to angiography, the science of visualizing blood vessels. He perfected the solution, first of sodium iodide, then of thorium dioxide, which once injected brought the vessels and arteries of the brain into relief on the X ray. These, in fact, were the first two substances to piove opaque to X rays without damaging the neural system. Moniz obtained the first cerebral arteriogram in man in the late 1920's. Without angiography, much of modern brain and heart surgery would be impossible.

Before attempting a wider application of lobotomy, Moniz intended to subject his twenty patients to a five-year period of intensive observation. To this he was faithful. But other neurosurgeons, hearing of his success through his monograph in 1936, themselves began refining the technique for the treatment of irremediable psychotics who had long ago exhausted all chances for cure. Doctors Walter Freeman and James Watts of George Washington University introduced the technique in America with their own improvements; Dr. E. Mariotti and Scuiti introduced it in Italy; Dr. F. Ody in Geneva, and still other surgeons influenced by these. Lobotomy experienced a popularity unrivaled in medicine—perhaps to its disadvantage.

This widespread application occasioned widespread criticism. More than one medical record charged psychosurgeons with mutilation, with polysurgical castration, with maiming and destroying the creative functions of their patients.

But the new technique weathered these criticisms.

In 1949, when Moniz won the Nobel Prize for Medicine, the citation read: ". . . [he] devised the revolutionary brain operation of prefrontal leucotomy, later known as lobotomy, now widely used in the treatment of certain forms of mental disease. In the last thirteen years . . . thousands of such operations, now modified into various patterns, have been carried out in many parts of the world, greatly to the betterment of patients with the more serious and prolonged types of mental aberration. A new psychiatry may be said to have been born in 1935 when Moniz took his first bold step into the field of psychosurgery."[5]

Criticism is leveled at every new therapy, if it is radical and if it is innovative. Psychosurgery was the next development after psychoanalysis. The mystical humanism of psychoanalysis unearths the past in order to let a patient enter the real present; the destructive attack of the psychosurgeon takes away tomorrow by stilling anxiety for the same reason. Both affect memory process. One is as important as the other. There is no past and there can be no future without today.

This is the story of Millard Wright, who offered to psychosurgery a mind undamaged by either psychosis or cellular deterioration. In 1947, Millard Wright agreed to undergo a frontal lobotomy. He was the first and only habitual criminal to risk this operation.

Wright had spent three tortuous decades in crime and in prisons, twenty-three even more terrifying months in a madhouse, and several doubt-ridden weeks before he asked a surgeon to perform this delicate operation. Yet the surgeon, once the possibility was suggested to him, said yes—yes because he wanted to bring man's newest scientific technique, neurosurgery, to bear on man's oldest, most persistent aberration, crime.

Certain doctors and patients find each other. They are drawn together, not like two magnets, but like two actors in a drama

[5] *A History of Neurological Surgery*, edited by A. Earl Walker. Baltimore: The Williams J. Wilkins Company, 1951, p. 285.

bringing a story to fulfillment, the doctor in achievement, the patient in health.

Millard Wright was such a patient, David Koskoff that doctor. They were more than doctor and patient, more than partners in a daring experiment, more, in fact, than friends; they became dependent upon each other for a common measure of success or failure, for a common gain or a common loss.

Part One
THE REPEATER

Chapter | I

Blairsville lies just over thirty miles due east of Pittsburgh on the Conemaugh River. In 1909 when Millard Filmore Wright was born it was still a rural farming community, its rolling hills occupied by trim red barns and neat, two-story white houses, each of the farms separated from the others by a stone wall or a split-rail fence. But the coal shanties of the miners were beginning to encircle the community as well as the jerrybuilt homes around the stone quarries and the clay pits. And there were many farmers who had sold off their fields and taken steady employment at the steel works in Conemaugh, five miles further east. Others had given up their dairy and poultry produce to work for the railroad and still others had gone into the mines. Rural America was just beginning the exodus from the countryside to the factories, offices, and industries of the city.

Not Malcolm Wright, Millard's father. Malcolm Wright was stone deaf, and had been stone deaf for the last eleven years. Neither he nor any doctor could determine why. Unable to hear the whistles, Wright couldn't work for the railroad; unable to hear the sound of danger he couldn't work in the coal mines or the steel mills. His scanty education made it impossible for him to work in an office as a clerk or bookkeeper. He was forced to be a laborer, working now for another farmer, now at the granary, now at the blacksmith's. Yet he managed well enough. He was thrifty, and he was a masterful carpenter. If he felt the slightest give in a banister, he straightaway repaired it and he would reset a window if he felt the slightest draft. He clothed and fed his four children adequately. He grew all the vegetables his family needed in a small plot, and with one cow and a few chickens the Wrights were self-sufficient the year round. He worked hard and long and he was never without employment of some kind. He could boast that whoever hired him got his money's worth.

He was also pious. A devout Presbyterian, he never missed a Sunday service at the brick church. At night, by the soft glow of a kerosene lamp, Malcolm Wright often sat at the oilcoth-covered kitchen table reading his Bible. From time to time, Lula Wright and the children prayed with him.

The house to which Malcolm Wright brought home his baby boy was small, compact, and sparsely furnished. It was a house, however, in which a family could live happily. The Wrights did not. There are tornadoes which sweep out of nowhere to demolish the foundations of a family.

Malcolm Wright had met the pleasant farm girl Lula Howard when he first emigrated from his native New York to Blairsville. She was a pretty girl, amiable and cheery, her devotion to him an accepted fact between both, never needing articulation. She was a good mother, too. The three girls, Edith, Lillian, and Mabel, obeyed without question any requests made of them. But when Lula came home after bearing Millard, she changed. She was cranky and short-tempered with the children and especially with the baby, who cried constantly and was always irritable. With a terrible moan one night, she abruptly left the table where Malcolm and the three girls prayed and without an explanation withdrew to the bedroom where she lay crying and groaning until the morning.

At first, Malcolm put her temper tantrums and her tears down to the baby, Millard. Millard was finicky about food and temperamentally refused his spoon time and time again. When Lula stopped the feeding, the little boy wailed in frustration. Though there had been no delay in toilet training any of the girls, Millard refused the discipline, which made Lula wring her hands impatiently. Millard, in fact, remained a bedwetter for a long time, which brought him shame and punishment. What had been an even, uneventful life for five people became ragged and careworn for six, and Malcolm Wright wondered what it was the little boy was doing to his mother.

In truth, little Millard was doing nothing to his mother. Probably it was his mother who was doing things to him, helplessly doing things to him. She was suffering from a relentless cancer, the pain of which was so intense that it interrupted life and duty more and more frequently. She never sought medical help until it was too late, although it is doubtful if medicine could have done much to save her. In her uninstructed way, Lula Wright imagined the terrible agony she suffered was in some way related to childbirth and would pass away. It is quite possible she blamed the baby for her ills and turned her back to him. Just before Millard Wright reached his third birthday, Lula died of a sarcoma of the uterus. She was thirty. Malcolm Wright never remarried. Edith, then eleven, became the mother of the Wright brood. And the bad luck persisted.

Edith had already suffered an attack of rheumatic fever; the heavy responsibilities made her health deteriorate even more. At odd hours in the day, she suddenly became dizzy; on other days she had to seek her bed and rest to regain her breath. The children went untended. But Malcolm Wright had no choice. Unsmiling, he left for work every morning and, unsmiling, he returned home every night.

Usually, the first thing he did was to ask Edith what had happened. She would tell him how Mabel and Lillian and Millard had behaved. Invariably, she had to tell him the little boy had wet his bed again. Night after night, Malcolm Wright confronted his child with this bad behavior. Since his father was deaf, Millard never had the chance to promise he would stop or to say he was sorry or to explain his own shame. While Millard did not live with terror by any means, neither did he live with any joy. He was the only boy and there was a necessary distance between him and his sisters. He never knew any real companionship with his father. There was no hunting, no fishing, no play or talk. His father was remote, shut up in a silent world bound only by work and sleep; the man was as far from him as the Allegheny Mountains, miles and miles away.

He knew his father as a figure who punished him and as a man who slept and disappeared just past dawn every morning.

One night, when he was eight, Millard ran away. The freight whistle from the railroad depot two miles away compelled him. Out of his pillowcase he fashioned a bindle and into it put his socks, washcloth, and clean Sunday clothes. When he knew the family was asleep, he shimmied down the rainspout and struck out for the freight yards. An hour later, a little tired, his bindle across his shoulder, he passed through the waiting room of the railroad station and tried sneaking into the freight yard some distance down the tracks. The ticket agent saw him. The agent called the yard police and within minutes a big jovial railroad dick laughingly confronted the runaway. It was Millard's first encounter with the law and his easiest, but no less significant for that. The policeman picked Millard up and demanded his name and after Millard told him, the man escorted him to a horse and rig and took him home.

As soon as the policeman left, Malcolm Wright gave Millard the usual strap-licking and afterward, defeated and despairing, the little boy made his way up the stairs, back to his room, tears streaking his face and sobs breaking from his throat.

Once asleep, he dreamt of a brutal bully pursuing him with a long curved knife. Still asleep, gripped by the nightmare, Millard tried to escape through the hall. He ran to the staircase and tumbled down its length, finally awakening to his own screams.

Fantasies of terror descended on Millard, not frequently but recurrently from then on. He was a lonely boy, isolated, left for days on end to his own amusements. He roamed the countryside, picking blueberries and strawberries in season, but he had never baited a hook or seen a baseball game. Like many little boys, he entertained himself with fantasies. He was a king as he sped down a hill, an explorer as he prowled through a deserted coal mine, a romantic hero with a wooden stave for a sword. But these fantasies often turned threatening suddenly and unexpectedly. He stepped on a dry branch which cracked, and his imagination made the broken wood into a coiling serpent with a flicking red tongue. Panic and fright washed over him. Fear spun him into random flight. Another terrifying fantasy overwhelmed him when he set off his hoarded store of blasting caps. The puff of acrid smoke which floated from the detonation convinced him he had started a raging forest fire, a hellfire which would consume the world. These were the times when Malcolm would return at dusk to find his son sobbing uncontrollably.

While Malcolm was kind and generous and comforting sometimes, there were other times when he was cruel and indifferent. He devised a punishment which could only confuse the boy. Whenever Millard strayed from the house or returned too late in the evening, he was made to wear one of his sisters' dresses. Wearing a dress confused Millard about the relationship he had with his father. Malcolm did not realize that his son often ran away to escape confusions. Every escape, however, was punished; running away only compounded Millard's confusion.

School provided Millard no relief or change. Perversity persisted in him. In class he was inattentive and disobedient. He always accepted his punishment, never sought to avoid it. Punishment in many ways fascinated him. He scrapped and too often with boys bigger than he. He took his lumps and returned home with torn clothes and a bloody nose. Usually the teacher had already punished him. Malcolm laid on as well. Between the clumsy efforts of teachers and father, Millard was bound to conceive a distrust for authority.

He played hookey. At ten he was a chronic truant, to the relief of his teacher. He was denied and denied himself the precise influence which might have shaped a better life for him—that of a strong, useful, and thoughtful adult. He found his own influence in the center of an insidious family named the Forshas.

In the conforming community, there is always that one family which, while perhaps not neglecting the law, neglects the community values or dismisses those values. They do not care. They are slovenly where the others are neat, idle when the others are busy, as disrespectful as the others are polite. The community resents them, resents them to a degree it never stops gossiping about them, never stops somehow envying them. The dismissal of values represents boldness: boldness implies vitality. Such were the Forshas. The natives of Blairsville called them "raggies."

Millard wanted to join the Forshas more out of curiosity than rebellion. One day he played truant from school and waited in the meadow until he was sure his father was at work, his sisters gone, the house deserted. He went to his room and carefully dressed himself in his dark blue Sunday suit with the full knickers, the Buster Brown collar, and the polished high-button shoes. Snapping on his black cap, he set off for the Forshas along the muddy road. Before noon, he was there. The rough Forsha boys saw him coming. They ran to the barn and climbed into the hayloft, leaving the youngest of their number as a lure.

Expectant Millard saw the boy beckon, then disappear into the barn. He followed. As he entered the musty barn, a load of manure descended upon him and he heard the whoops from the ambushers above.

Blinking back his tears, Millard bent to retrieve his cap. He brushed his suit, soiled now beyond cleaning, and faced the ruffians clambering down the ladder. Crook Forsha, who earned his nickname because of a mouth permanently disfigured by a harelip, came forward and said, "You *are* game. Not bad. What's your name?"

"Millard Wright."

"Want to rob Turner's apple orchard with us?"

"Let's go," said Millard. He had found playmates.

Ben Forsha, the father, was lazy and shiftless, now and then holding a job, but never for long. He had a well-deserved reputation as a petty thief. He never disciplined his sons. Instead he encouraged their forays.

As soon as Crook Forsha, two of his brothers, and Millard returned from the Turner orchard, struggling with a heavy bushel basket, Ben Forsha divided the plunder equitably enough except he expropriated a share for himself.

That night, when Millard brought home his apples, Malcolm beat his son with such ferocity that the blood flowed down Millard's legs from the flailing belt buckle. The beating did not deter him. He had found a reward. The Forshas had introduced him to risk. Risk gave him pleasure, excitement, and self-importance.

There were more forays into Turner's apple orchards and among McDaniel's peach trees. Hammers and nails and a small hatchet disappeared from the hardware store. Millard expertly swept small change from the marble counter of the soda fountain. Though younger, Millard was the equal of Crook Forsha in daring.

The supreme adventure came the day that one of the Erie-Lackawanna freight trains hopped the rails just outside of Blairsville. One of the freight cars, torn from its couplings, tumbled down the embankment, spilling its contents. Half a ton of candy lay on the tracks for the taking. Nor were Millard and the Forsha brothers the only predators. All of the Blairsville children scrambled along the rails to fill their mouths and their pockets with gumdrops, chocolate cherries, and peppermint wafers. Most of these children had more than satisfied themselves when the wrecking crew came along, followed by a crane on a flat car. They shooed the boys and girls away. Millard left too but he took up a station behind a clump of trees, watching as the crew maneuvered the crane to the boxcar, righted it, lifted it back onto the tracks and sent it grinding slowly off to the freight yard where Millard guessed it would be shifted to a siding. Carefully he memorized the boxcar's number.

That evening Millard led Crook and another Forsha to the yards and silently they stole along the rows of bulking boxcars, lighting matches now and then to check the numbers. They found the car they were looking for. By this time, it had its sides shored up and the sliding doors were clasped by a strong lock. With one wrench of a short crowbar, Millard tore the hasp, slid back the door, and jumped in to throw the candy out to the two Forshas, who stuffed it in a large flour bag. They were careless. The matches sparking the night, the rasp of metal tearing from wood alerted the railroad guards, who made quickly toward the car. The two Forshas saw them. They dropped their bag and ran. Millard submitted meekly to a gruff voice behind a blinding lantern.

The next morning, the county squire fined Malcolm Wright twenty-five dollars for Millard's trespass. Twenty-five dollars was more than a week's pay. Malcolm vowed, "You will not cost me that again." He beat the boy and kept him locked within his room for the next three weeks.

To keep Millard away from the Forshas, Malcolm moved from Blairsville to Smith Station, a smaller town some miles away. For a while the strategy worked. Millard mended his ways. Dutifully he went to school and inspired no mischief. Until he discovered the Butlers.

The Butlers were not the outlaws the Forshas were, but Mr. Butler was as lazy and as slovenly as Ben. His house was always in disrepair and his unused farm tools rusted in the barn. He was a kinder man, however, and liked to tell stories about the Civil War which enthralled Millard. His three sons were reckless but with none of the viciousness of the Forshas. Mrs. Butler wasn't yet worn from work and sadness. She liked Millard and even worried about him, frequently setting an extra place for him at her table because she thought him too thin and undernourished.

The Butlers took to Millard because he knew so much about the Forshas. There was a feud between the two families. The feud had its locus not in wrongs, real or fancied, but in the fact that the two families so resembled each other that the community— and the police—often mistook them, which damaged the pride of both. This hostility surfaced when the Forshas learned that Millard was now friendly with the Butlers. Crook Forsha and his brothers walked the ten miles to Smith Station to comfront Millard with his disloyalty. Crook even advanced on Millard. But the oldest boy, George Butler, intervened, and the Forshas withdrew. Gratitude flooded Millard and he realized an important fact: His allegiance was worth something. He had grasped that Crook's threats were not an attempt to punish him, but to reclaim him. Cannily, he saw that he could profess loyalty to both families. If the Butlers were anxious to hear gossip about the Forshas, then probably the Forshas were just as anxious to hear about the Butlers. Thereafter he played one family off against the other. He was learning elementary manipulation and compromise.

He could even use this technique with his father, who always questioned him closely about how he had spent the day. Now Millard lied. He named the boys of whom his father approved. Never at ease with his father, he adopted a strategy of constant deception. He commuted between three sets of values—those of the Butlers, those of the Forshas, and those of his father, never picking up any for himself.

Millard, now eleven years old, still had trouble reading. He needed prompting, a fact which puzzled his teachers because he had a normal and active intelligence. One of his teachers persuaded the school nurse to bring Millard to an ophthalmologist in Pittsburgh. The diagnosis was quick. Millard had keratoconus, a congenital eye defect in which the cornea is conical instead of crescentic. He was also myopic and astigmatic. While glasses would help, they would never correct this deficiency. He was slow reading because the world he saw was a distorted world, had always been distorted, and would remain distorted. But thereafter he loved reading, and read constantly, even though it caused him fatigue and physical pain.

At this time, Edith, just eighteen, married a man named John Livengood and moved with him to Blairsville. Though he had never thought Edith was particularly kind to him, Millard cried, never quite sure why, on the day she married. Her marriage changed the routine of Malcolm Wright's household. Lillian and Mabel were not as willing as their older sister to assume responsibility. Grudgingly, they kept house for Malcolm until they tired of quiet Smith Station with no young men for them to meet. They too left for Blairsville and found work as waitresses. Millard was left to care for his father. He cooked the meals and did the housework. He steamed the laundry in a copper-bottomed tub, swirling it around with a large laundry pestle. He helped Malcolm do the modest shopping. He proved much more efficient than Lillian and Mabel. Malcolm gave his son two rewards: He told him he was like his mother, a remark Millard took to mean he was his father's favorite; and he bought Millard a .22 rifle for his twelfth birthday.

Millard lined up the tin cans and the shards of broken bottles and kept firing at them until he learned accuracy. Then he began shooting at flying birds. Within months he was able to wing a bird in flight—any bird, a sparrow, a blue jay, a robin. He spent hours killing birds, watching raptly as the bird toppled from the air and plummeted earthward.

"I think you shoot too many things," Malcolm said one night when they were sitting on the back porch.

"Just birds." Millard shrugged.

"Shoot crows," said the father. "Every farmer shoots crows. Kill all the robins and you have a farm filled with worms."

"Just birds," Millard repeated. He sighted the .22 at a black-capped chickadee hopping along the ground. His father watched him as he fired. The bird fell over, its breast shattered.

"You go too far," Malcolm said and disappeared into the house.

A few days later, proud of the rifle and his marksmanship, Millard walked the ten miles to the Forshas. The brothers whooped when they saw him and clustered around as he showed them how to load and aim. They in turn, showed him their new acquisition, a battered Ford that Ben Forsha had somehow salvaged. Crowded into the car, Millard and all the Forsha brothers tore down the dirt roads, stopping now and then to fire the rifle at mallards navigating the neighborhood ponds. It was late when they came back to the Forshas' and though they had promised to drive Millard there was no gasoline left.

It was dark and Millard took a long time getting home. The single kerosene lamp illumined Malcolm, seated at the kitchen table, a razor strop across his knees. He had fried his own eggs, eaten them, and now waited impatiently for Millard's explanation.

"I went over to show the Forshas the new rifle," Millard answered.

"The Forshas?" repeated Malcolm. He always repeated words he wanted particularly to understand.

"The Forshas," said Millard defiantly.

"You disobeyed me," said the father. "You saw the Forshas. You didn't cook my dinner."

"I cook and clean for you all the time," said Millard.

Malcolm's face colored. He tested the strop against his hand and, voice rising, began, "There is no worth in you, Millard. You are a bad boy, a cross to bear. You are heartless and ungrateful. I have cared for you, been both your mother and your father. I've told you stories, fed and clothed you, tried to give you a start in this world. You never repay me. You are cruel. I've seen you cruel. You love to kill birds. You disobey. Well, you won't disobey anymore."

He advanced with the strop.

Millard raised the rifle to this shoulder. He aimed at Malcolm. Malcolm saw his eyes squint. The boy meant it. Malcolm did the one thing he thought could spare him. He threw the razor strop on the table. Millard's face relaxed. He lowered the rifle.

They went to bed without another word. In the morning, the rifle was gone. Malcolm had confiscated it. Millard resolved he would have his rifle back or one just like it.

In the barn, there was a bore from an old squirrel gun. Taking it, Millard went over to the Forshas and they scoured the barns of the nearby farms until they found an old worm-eaten stock. Millard fitted them together. Of course the rifle wouldn't fire; it had neither trigger mechanism nor breech.

None of the boys were gunsmiths and Millard sighed that this would have to do. He was about to leave when Crook saw a wagon coming down the road, its team tended by a half-slumbering man.

"Look at the old hunky," said Crook. "Lost and drunk. Doesn't know where he is or where he's going."

"Let's have some fun with him," said Millard. "Let's stick him up."

They stationed themselves behind the trees along the road until the team and wagon drew abreast. Crook and his brothers commanded in unison, "Stick 'em up! Stick 'em up!" The driver shook his head and tried to focus his sleepy eyes. At this moment Millard stepped from behind a tree, the rifle at the ready.

Instinctively, the driver snapped his whip and the horses lunged, found purchase, and the wagon careened past. The old man put his hands to his head and ducked low. With no hand on the reins, the horses galloped frenziedly and the driver bounced on the hard wooden seat like a rag doll.

Millard and the Forshas laughed and laughed as the wagon disappeared down the road. It was good fun. But an hour later the sheriff drove out to the Forshas' and made all the boys get into the back seat of the car. He remained deaf to their explanations. All he asked was, "Which one of you had the gun? Which one?"

"I did," said Millard. "But it wouldn't fire. It was just a play gun."

Millard spent his first night in jail.

Ben Forsha was there in the morning to reclaim his sons. He apologized abjectly to the man on the bench, who, fixing the Forshas with a hard eye, gave them a half-hour lecture on the meaning of assault.

Malcolm Wright wasn't there. Malcolm Wright had spent the night remembering orders willfully disobeyed, remembering a rifle pointed straight at him.

The squire didn't bother to lecture Millard. He said, "You have once been arrested for pilfering. Now you have been arrested for attempted robbery. I am going to send you to Oakdale on the charge of incorrigibility. When you learn to behave yourself, you'll get out."

Chapter | 2

Oakdale, one of the reformatories for western Pennslyvania, took its name from the small town in Indiana County on whose outskirts it was located. The wooden barracks, the work sheds, the mess hall, and the administration shack were new, as new as the theory which supposedly animated the institution. At Oakdale, corporal punishment was a last resort. It was a correctional institution and the education boys received there was to prepare them for life as useful citizens.

A State Legislature had once agreed to this—in spirit—congratulating itself as it warmed to a young supervisor with new ideas, new methods. But then the complex, which included dormitories with spacious rooms, well-equipped machine shops, an auditorium, a swimming pool, and desk-equipped classrooms came before an appropriations committee. The committee, thinking of the state budget, erased everything. Now, narrow cots lined uninsulated pinewood barracks, heated only by barrel stoves; the cathedral roofs gave way to hastily tacked tar paper; the gardens and the hedges that lined the entrance became instead barbed wire, pinned to high stakes in billowing rolls. None of the boys learned machine skills and none of them faced a blackboard. In gray pants and striped shirts they worked the dusty farm which surrounded Oakdale, and in the winter they cleared the snow-bound roads and chopped the wood which heated them at night. There were no whips in Oakdale, but the guards—all of them political appointees, the wayward cousins and foolish friends of men who merited patronage—all wore thick heavy belts with big steel buckles. And they swung shiny clubs.

All that remained of the original vision was the welcoming speech to new inmates which the supervisor still delivered in ringing, hopeful tones.

Millard found Oakdale's regimen taxing but not exhausting. He was assigned by the supervisor to clean the wooden latrines on the west side of the complex and to spend the rest of the day on the garbage detail. Each day he and the other boys rose just past daybreak and after a breakfast of hot mush and watery cocoa reported to their detail guard. They worked till noon, marched to the mess hall for a meal which, in the summer, consisted of vegetables, fruits, and warm potatoes and in the winter of soup, and worked until the late afternoon. On rare occasions they had meat for their dinner meal, but their usual fare was cereal and potatoes.

In the summer, they went to sleep when the sun set. In the winter, they waited until one of the guards twisted off the one electric bulb which illuminated each of the barracks.

Millard also learned one of the bitter truths about society's mass institutions. It is hard enough to obey and satisfy the authorities who control life, but it can be managed if one can exist anonymously in the eyes of those authorities. It is harder to live with the inmates because one cannot live anonymously with them at all. Frustrated and often despairing, the inmates turn upon the weakest among them for assertion. That assertion, of course, menaces the anonymity of the weakest, making him fair game for the authorities.

Which is precisely what the city toughs did to Millard, who was their junior by several years. They tripped him when he labored with the heavy garbage cans, they gave him mischievous directions when he asked them about certain regulations, they mussed his cot after he had made it. He ached with loneliness and in the two hours each day he had to himself, he crept into the locker room, where he pitied himself silently. The guards mistook this torment for sullen brooding. By making himself remote, Millard worked against acceptance.

He had been at Oakdale a month when one day two of the guards came upon him in the locker room.

"Someone rifled that locker," said one guard, pointing. "You?"

"No," said Millard in amazement.

"It had to be you. Who else is in the locker room?"

"But I didn't," Millard protested.

"We'll teach you," said the second guard. He grasped Millard by the wrist and wrestled him outside and into the center of the compound, while the first guard blew several shrill blasts on his whistle. In no time, a ring of boys formed around the two grown guards and Millard, who was struggling to free himself. The second guard released Millard.

"Drop your pants!" he ordered. Then again, more threateningly, "Drop your pants." Millard obeyed. The boys in the ring hooted.

"Now bend over and hold your ankles."

The leather belt cracked across him twice.

When Millard, gasping, straightened up, his hands protecting his rump, the guard pushed his head down and struck.

Again and again he struck the fourteen-year-old boy.

Tears blinded Millard. Injustice outraged him. Mortification fueled the rage. Not only did he know he had not stolen, but his instincts told him there had been no theft. The guards had never sought to recover whatever was missing. Millard was simply an instrument, an example to the others, his guilt or innocence of no concern to anyone, his pain a matter of laughter.

Two nights later, he crawled on all fours into the locker room, surreptitiously removed his clothes from the locker, and snakelike wriggled under the barbed wire. It took him two days to cover the sixty miles to Smith Station.

Malcolm told him, "I'll let bygones be bygones."

"But they will come to get me," Millard said.

"No," said Malcolm. "Not a Wright. They won't find a Wright. Not if we put our minds to it."

"Where can I go?" asked Millard. "This is the only home I know."

"I'll apprentice you to the Oberdorffs. They need a chore boy. They won't find you there."

In the morning, Malcolm brought Millard a pair of dungarees and two work shirts. He rented a car and drove him twenty-five miles along back roads to the Oberdorff farm. Mr. Oberdorff was happy to have extra help. He was an old man and his wife was even older. Their orchard covered several dozen acres and they had several hogs and a small dairy.

"Can you work it?" Mr. Oberdorff asked.

"Yes," said Millard.

"Well, if you can work it, we can let you sleep in the dormer," said Mr. Oberdorff.

Millard did work the orchard and the dairy, worked them well enough to sit evenings with the Oberdorffs, pour cream over his apple pie, and talk about the next day's chores to the Dutchman over coffee. When Millard lit the old man's meerschaum, Mr. Oberdorff puffed contentedly and wondered politely if Millard had time to prune the east orchard.

As the month went by, Millard forgot he had ever been at Oakdale. The day was always long enough to finish each of the chores he had to do. Every morning Mrs. Oberdorff fried him several eggs and served him toast which she made by putting a piece of bread on the stove lid and an iron on top of that. At noon she came out to the fields carrying a lunch basket filled with cold ham slices and apple kooken.

He was home.

But only for a little while.

A county detective burst open the Oberdorff front door one night, and as the three startled people looked up from the table, he put manacles around Millard's wrists. It was going to take Millard a long time to learn how to become a prisoner.

Chapter | 3

Millard had been at Oakdale long enough to have heard about "Morgan." Morgan was the nickname for Morganza, a reformatory fifteen miles south of Pittsburgh. It drew its inmates not from the offices of a county squire or a juvenile court judge but from other reformatories, and from impatient parole officers.

From his barred window, Millard, his shorn skull daubed with Tincture of Larkspur to kill lice, looked out on walls. Inside these walls were a rude school building, beside it several workshops and the rows upon rows of whitewashed cells. Outside were farms, each of them patrolled by a guard in a blue suit cradling a shotgun.

Millard didn't live in a barracks any more, he lived in a cell with a canvas cot suspended from the wall by two strong chains. A loud buzzer warned him to rise, to eat, and to sleep.

The boys in a column of twos peeled out of their cells in the morning in silence. The reformatory filled with the tread of marching feet echoing off the concrete walls. Hearing that tramp every morning, every night, being part of it, could not help but deaden sensibility. And Millard would spend twenty months at Morgan, crucial months for a growing boy.

Millard entered the seventh grade of the prison school. Only four years before he had learned to read. Now he read rapidly and with comprehension. All his life, in fact, Millard would pride himself on his ability to read intensely; although he comprehended difficult and complex books, that comprehension never effectively enlarged his imagination or modified his behavior. In a classroom where he was for the most part surrounded by illiterates and boys incapable of learning, Millard strutted. He had to prove to everyone his mind was precision-tooled. That he was able to read at all impressed the county-assigned teacher. But Millard, boasting about his facility, made his classmates jealous, more than jealous. He often infuriated them, for he became the gauge by which the teacher measured their efforts. This teacher assigned punishment for inattention. Millard broke one of the cardinal rules for convicts: obey but do not cooperate.

He was headed for a desperate encounter with these boys, an encounter which might have done him good, taught him the world can literally force adjustments upon us, when he and two other classmates contracted scarlet fever. Too listless to leave the classroom, their eyes glazed, their faces reddening perceptibly, they were in near delirium when the teacher called for Henry Glanz, Morganza's supervisor. Henry Glanz drove the three feverish boys that afternoon to Municipal Hospital in Pittsburgh and the doctors immediately isolated them in the contagious-disease ward.

Millard proved an ideal patient. The fever let him relax. He found for the first time that helpless weakness required that others care for him. There was a large streak of passivity in Millard's nature. This hospital stay was the first time others served that passivity. The nurses were solicitous. The doctors made constant inquiries. It was all soothing and comforting.

Of the three patients, Millard was the youngest and he received the most care. He recovered first. Within a few days, he was able to sit up in his bed, alert, the fever abated, the recipient of luxurious attention while the other two boys, Duke and Stanislaus, languished in torpor. Millard was rather disappointed when they recovered.

Duke and Stanislaus frightened him. They wanted to escape. Millard argued that Mr. Glanz had put them on their honor.

Keeping their honor, they sneered, meant stitching an awful lot of burlap.

Still Millard refused. They called him yellow and one night stole away.

Henry Glanz was there the next noon, asking Millard where the two boys had gone. Millard replied he didn't know. Glanz asked him if he was going to run away too. Millard promised he would not. The supervisor left him, and Millard stayed on two months. He had never felt safer than in the hospital. Once he was able to get up, which was within the week, he helped the nurses make their rounds through the other wards. He was a helpful boy and polite. The nurses liked him, made him their pet, clucked sympathetically when he described the way in which he had come to Morgan.

He spent much of his time in the hospital library, reading Zane Grey, James Oliver Curwood, and Ralph Connor, delighting in the contest between courage and despair. In those two months his provocative and defensive posture relaxed; love and affection, the romances which fed his yearning began to refine and refocus his vision of the distorted angular world so forbidding till now.

When Millard returned to Morganza, Henry Glanz rewarded him. Millard was not assigned to one of the cell block dormitories, but to one of the cottages reserved for the trustworthy. In that rewarding gesture, Henry Glanz unwittingly undid all the good the hospital had done. For Millard, as a trustee, lived with Roy Sloan, an eighteen-year-old criminal, hardened by his own acts, devious, yet brilliant, and smart enough to abide the sentence he must serve.

Roy Sloan was the son of Hedwig Sjanderstrom, a Swedish journalist, who had written an ephemeral novel which had nevertheless made her into an immediate if minor celebrity. Roy Sloan's father had been an itinerant sculptor who had long since drifted away from son and mother. Like Millard, Roy Sloan had been left to his own devices at an early age, not on a farm with chores to perform, but in a spacious Philadelphia home, tended by servants, tutors, and a governess, with occasional trips to Europe. All these things conspired to make him into a clever and consistently expert forger. Several times he fleeced store owners, putting false signatures to charge accounts, forging checks, quickly disposing of the material; and several times, because of his youth and his mother's literary position, judges had forgiven him. But he came before the same judge twice, a judge who had already sternly and indignantly warned him; with great dispatch the judge sent him to Morganza and his mother, busy with her own celebrity, decided Roy simply took up too much of her time. She calmed her conscience with an occasional visit whenever her entertaining and her lectures permitted.

The reformatory granted Roy preferential treatment. He gained this preference not because of any outside influence or pressure, but because he was an absolutely charming, poised, and glib young man. He had a preparatory school education, a wide range of sophistication—far more than his guards, let alone his fellow prisoners—and a self-confidence that was never disturbed. He was, in short, an impressive boy, just the sort to attract the attention of Morgan's administrators, who often despaired of accomplishing rehabilitation. They might have spared themselves the trouble. Roy might have looked gold, down at bottom he was brass. He was a phony and that is why prison attracted him—in it he glittered.

He lorded it over Millard. No sooner was Millard quartered with him than Hedwig Sjanderstrom passed through on one of her infrequent visits. She was, literally, a society lady, one dressed fashionably with marcelled blond hair; a woman who wore gloves in the summer and a big flat hat dripping with imitation flowers.

Roy introduced Millard, already seduced by Hedwig's glamour. Mrs. Sloan extended her hand, on which jewels sparkled, and Millard, holding it briefly, was in Roy's debt. Roy exploited this subservience. He basked in all the admiration he could extract from Millard, and Millard was lavish with admiration. Roy wanted a spotlight and he didn't care from whence it shone, nor how dim.

"Why do you read those magazines?" Millard asked him once, pointing to the *Saturday Evening Post*, the *American*, and the *Atlantic*.

"They are in good taste," answered Roy. "They are educational. Not like Zane Grey."

To Millard, profound reasons. He accepted without disclaimer that Zane Grey was somehow suspect, just as he accepted everything Roy told him. Consequently it was easy for Roy to dazzle Millard with tales of the adventuresome and challenging world of crime.

Roy was everything Millard was not: an arch-criminal where Millard was a fumbler; a sophisticate where Millard was a rube; a man of family where Millard was the castaway son of an impoverished deaf man; a gentleman where Millard only aspired to occasional grace. Roy was the ideal: the glorified version of the confused self, a crystallized version of the evolving Millard.

After six months in the honor cottage, Henry Glanz transferred Millard to the new infirmary his wife had set up for Morganza inmates. Had she established this six months earlier and put Millard to work in it, it might, just might, have made a crucial difference in his attitudes. As it was, Millard was vastly disappointed and angry at separation from his hero. Now he hated serving others who were ill, although the sick boys as well as Mrs. Glanz trusted him and did all they could to give him a sense of personal worth. Working in the hospital also took him out of school, a place where he thought he exercised the natural superiority of his mind over others.

The State of Pennsylvania returned Millard to his father in the summertime of 1926, aged sixteen. He came home not to Smith Station but to Black Lick, a town a few miles north of Blairsville. Malcolm Wright had moved to a smaller home and though he welcomed Millard undemonstratively, the boy thought his father was glad to see him.

They talked the first night home about a fresh start, about the new surroundings. Bygones were bygones. Millard forbore asking his father why no letters, why no visits, why no encouragement?

Chapter | 4

Millard thought he and his father had changed their relationship, moving into a warmer, more personal friendship, that they were ideally at last father and son. But the truth was simply that Millard had grown older, seen more; though most of what he had seen was shabby, his view of life was broader than Malcolm's. Nor could Malcolm help but notice that Millard read and read seriously. Malcolm was of that generation who subscribed not so much to education as to books: books were the mark of the good, the successful, the rich man. Millard was also robust. He had grown and his form was filling out. Malcolm told him, "If the mule ever dies, those shoulders of yours can pull a plow, don't worry."

The day after Millard came home, he went to visit his friends the Butlers, but he found the farmhouse and barn gone. The land now supported a ring of cheap new houses, some of them not more than five months old. No one seemed to know exactly what had happened to the family. Millard next walked the ten miles to Blairsville to see the Forshas. He was in love that morning with the warm summer air, the trees which rustled slightly as a light breeze brushed their leaves, the open road, the sound of men working in the fields—the gratuitous values of a bright day.

The Forshas put a damper on his spirits. They didn't ask him to dinner, nor did they propose an adventure. It pained Millard to learn there was a difference between those who had served time and those who hadn't.

A week later, with Malcolm's help, Millard found a job as a carpenter's helper. He made forty cents an hour—twenty-four dollars every week, appreciable money for a sixteen-year-old boy.

He left his home in the early morning and walked to Main Street where he boarded a trolley, and rode down the pike to Blairsville. The trolley accommodated the same passengers day after day, all of them bound for work at the same hour, all of them on a nodding acquaintance.

Although Millard was shy, he had no trouble participating in the casual chatter and laughter that carried the passengers along. And as soon as he did so, he saw that a pretty girl with dark hair and round green eyes always laughed first at what he said. Millard was pale, withdrawn, and he wore glasses. All of which created an aura of appealing defenselessness—which made him attractive to aggressive girls.

She told him her name was Elizabeth, a name which pleased Millard because it suggested royalty. She said, "Come see me after dinner."

A girl. Maybe his girl. Magic at the end of the day. Millard faithfully followed the ritual. He bathed, he changed his clothes, shined his shoes, combed and recombed his hair; he did everything to prepare himself for that luminous presence.

When he came to her house, he made the traditional suggestion—"We can go the Gem." All the language he could manage.

"Oh, no," she said, turning to the hammock on the front porch, "let's not go to the movies. Let's sit here and talk."

They talked. They talked about what she did, with whom she worked, her mother's maiden name. He told her about his sisters in Blairsville, about his father's deafness, about his mother's death. They held hands as they rocked back and forth, so interested the one in the other, they never heard the squeaks.

Millard saw Elizabeth several times each week. Each night they kissed on the hammock. Gallantly, Millard finally proposed they make love.

"No," said Elizabeth, removing his arm from her shoulder.

They sat quietly for a few seconds and Millard said meekly, "I'm sorry."

She turned her back to him.

"I won't ask again."

Nor did he. Millard never repeated skirmishes which could lead to direct attack. If only he hadn't asked, he was pretty sure her excitement would have made her succumb. But he didn't like aggression. Aggression was for the rough and unrefined, not for those who would emulate the calm poise of Roy Sloan. Millard's approach was romantic, chivalrous, gentle, effective. Millard rather preferred his inhibitions.

The trip by trolley every morning was such an inhibition; true, it was an inhibition suffused with pleasure, but still a situation which demanded restraint. It was accepted that they sit together, but their talk was always idle, always hedged by the pretense they were only casual acquaintances.

Once when Elizabeth inadvertently called Millard "Lov'ems," the boys who stood in the well by the conductor whooped and whipped their gaze around from the front window. They too called Millard "Lov'ems," and he bore with a blush the knowledge that for Elizabeth to call him "Lov'ems" was worth any possible embarrassment.

But one morning one of the boys yelled, "Hey, Crook Forsha says to stop calling you 'Lov'ems.' He says you're tough. He says call you Morganza Pete. You want us to call you Morganza Pete or 'Lov'ems'?"

The girls giggled. The other boys guffawed. The men and women kept a discreet silence. Millard saw they all knew. That moment dissipated the warmth and friendship of the trolley community. Gossips! They were all against him. Shame paralyzed him. He might have remained immobile and weathered this shame if one of the boys hadn't begun singing: "They call him Morganza Pete. We'll put him on the street . . ." He got no further because Millard was up and advancing, fists clenched. With that the conductor brought the trolley to a stop. "Out," he barked. "The three of you. Out." He levered open the door. "I mean it," he said. "Out. And stay out until you learn to ride like gentlemen."

Elizabeth obviously enjoyed the gesture. She waved good-bye to Millard as the trolley pulled off. The fight in the three youths was overcome by the unceremonious eviction. The other two walked on to work. The humiliation tortured Millard. He raged. He walked home, and walking home that morning, lost his job.

He did not tell Malcolm why he was without work. He lied. He said the carpenter had run out of houses; he'd have to find something else. Millard had worked long enough to accumulate twenty dollars in savings. With this as a down payment, he bought a 1923 Model-T Ford, claiming he had to have it to find new employment. Malcolm frowned disapprovingly but said nothing. *He'd* never had a car in his life.

Millard's reform was over, for he had persuaded himself, half in anger and half in earnest, that it was useless. He drove over to the Forshas' and accosted Crook.

"You told people about Morganza."

"Naw," said Crook, "everybody knows. What are you worried about?"

"It's my girl. They told her on the trolley."

"I'll get you a girl," said Crook. "I'll get you a girl easy if we can use the car. Where'dya get it?"

"Bought it," said Millard.

"Shows what work will do for a man," said Crook.

Millard couldn't help himself. He felt drawn to Crook. He had come flaming over Crook's betrayal and now he was about to drive him though the side streets of little Pennsylvania towns, laughing and joking, betrayal buried in expectation. What attracted him in Crook, though Millard did not know it, was what had attracted him in Roy Sloan: Crook and Roy were devious, wily men. Roy wore a more fashionable mask but Crook was bolder. They were alike, so alike both would die in silk shirts —Crook, writhing on a curb, tearing for a bullet in his groin from the gun of a bank guard, his death struggles never disturbing the buttoned coat, the silver tie, the stick pin, his oozing blood never staining the breast of the shiny white shirt; and Roy, walking to the electric chair in New York for the murder of a wealthy widow, wearing, as his last request, a silk shirt with the collar torn off.

But Millard couldn't know this, now touring the mine towns

with Crook, the hope of becoming a man with a woman inspiring him. One late afternoon, they passed two sisters, rough girls in their teens, who responded with a wave to whistles. Millard and Crook drove them out to an old country road, then, pairing off, followed a mule trail down to a pine-encircled lake.

Millard's girl said her name was Ann, and that her sister's was Mary. Millard could hear Mary and Crook wrestling and laughing and he put his arm around Ann and pawed her. "I want a dollar," she said.

He gave her a dollar—he had exactly four quarters and a dime. She certainly didn't take him for a big shot. She said with a shrug, "A dollar's a dollar," and lay back and hiked up her skirt. His first sex was easy enough. She grunted once or twice and all that frightened him was that she wrapped her legs around his waist. He wondered if she would have a baby. Finished, she slipped from under him, sat up, and brushed her dirty blond hair from her forehead.

When they left the girls halfway down a darkened street, Millard tried one last affectionate embrace. "You had enough squeezing for one night," Ann said to him. "You can meet me again. Right here. Any evening. Bring a dollar bill next time."

Millard certainly intended meeting her again, but he never did. Nine days later, he confided nervously in Crook, "It keeps dripping. It's hard to piss. What could it be?"

"You got clap," said Crook. "Good for you. You're not a man until you've had a dose."

"She did it when she put her legs around me," Millard said.

Crook said he knew a doctor in Blairsville. "He'll fix you right up. Takes no time at all."

The doctor's advertisement promised his ministrations could remedy acne, consumption, and any pelvic inflammatory diseases, the euphemism of the day for gonorrhea. He gave Millard some pills and told him to come back the next day, and he repeated these instructions the next day, and the day after that. The constriction persisted and passing water was agony for Millard. He stopped confiding in Crook and drove himself to Pittsburgh, to the Municipal Hospital, where he awaited his turn in the clinic, sure that he would be recognized by the nurses and doctors he had known two years before.

The doctor said matter-of-factly, "Yes, you have gonorrhea. Where did you pick it up?"

"In a public toilet," Millard said as though no man had ever offered the same excuse.

"Funny place to take a woman," said the doctor.

"What is it?" asked Millard when he saw a small steel rod in the doctor's hands.

"Romeo's wand," said the doctor. "Also known as a sounds. I'm going to have to straighten out your urinary canal before we drain you."

"Does it hurt?"

"One fellow told me he'd be better off putting it on a sill, closing his eyes, and slamming the window, but then he was older." The pain persuaded Millard sex was not a source of joy but a form of defeat. Later, the doctor flushed the germs with permanganate solution and sent home a chastened, still-frightened, guilt-ridden boy.

It surprised him that Elizabeth Burt sought him out again. He could not face her with his shame. She thought it was his sentence in Morganza that burdened him. She asked him to take her to a dance, insisted upon it. Millard agreed finally, not only because she mitigated his shame but because he knew neither of them chose to pursue a sexual relationship.

Millard always retained a quiet charm which attracted women. What particularly attracted Elizabeth, however, was his pliability. He lent himself readily to her manipulations. She could easily create contention over herself, battle situations which enlarged her ego.

The Fireman's Ball at Black Lick was a community affair for which a girl needed an escort, but she was certainly free to dance with whom she chose and was expected to dance with all the boys who asked. Yet Millard had no sooner finished his first turn around the wooden platform than a young neighbor of Elizabeth's accosted him.

"I don't want you dancing with her anymore."

"You don't?" asked Millard. "Why not?"

"You have no right to," said the boy.

"Make it stick," said Millard. Slowly but deliberately, he removed his eyeglasses and took off his coat. He handed them to the thrilled Elizabeth. The boy was bigger than Millard with muscles hardened from farmwork. Millard hadn't the slightest doubt about who was the better fighter: the farmboy. But Millard had suffered beatings before and though the prospect of another one dismayed him, it didn't strike the terror his opponent supposed.

The willingness to fight put off the farmboy. He walked away. If the socially acute situation she caused flattered Elizabeth, it did more than that for Millard. Chancing it made Millard a gladiator. He was always a gladiator without a smile; he never laughed over his victories—they relieved rather than pleased him. Risk made his personality more viable. He took too many. Risk was something he should have avoided, yet Elizabeth kept multiplying them. She was bad medicine.

A few days after this episode, Millard found a job at the Conemaugh Iron Works in Blairsville. Now he drove to work and avoided the trolley. He was a helper for one of the repairmen and traversed the factory pushing a loaded repair flat. There was an urgency to the work; he and the repairman were always on the go, and the day passed quickly.

After a week, however, his boss said ominously, "You're the punk that's seeing Lizzie aren't you?"

"Elizabeth Burt?"

"Yes," said the man. "She used to be my girl before you turned her head. Johnny Smith backed off at the ball, but I won't. You stay away from her."

"I didn't know about you and her. But don't tell me what to do. If Elizabeth wants to see me, I'll see her and I don't care if the foreman of the Iron Works tells me not to."

The repairman tried a shove which Millard dodged.

"You try that again," he warned, "and you'll chew on this fist for lunch."

"We'll see who chews what fist for lunch. In the yard," said the repairman.

The fight lasted one blow, Millard's. There wasn't even time for the other steelworkers to form a ring, make their bets, and shout the fighters on. Millard struck first and hard, and the repairman went down, striking his head on the railroad tracks. He

THE REPEATER | 31

groaned once, tried to roll over, raised his hand feebly where a bad cut began bleeding, and lay back.

Two of the other steelworkers and Millard carried the man to the first-aid office.

With the repairman gone, there was little for Millard to do except tend the loaded flat. By this time the rumor of the scuffle had circulated through the entire mill. Apprehension colored the afternoon. Finally the foreman came over to the flat and fired Millard.

He was without a job once more and once more in disgrace.

The next evening, he and Crook Forsha, in the Model-T, drove slowly through back streets looking for dates. Even that furtive preoccupation ended when the right front tire went flat. Millard and Crook tried repairing it with the few patches they still had in the tin repair kit but the inner tube was worn. The two boys were stranded outside a mining town. They sat on the running board of the car, its hood still jacked high, and began planning how to get home.

"I saw a farmhouse down the road with a truck in the garage," said Crook.

Millard tossed the empty repair kit aside and started walking. Crook followed. They crept along the hedge and waited until they saw the last bedroom light flick off. Hurriedly they ran to the garage and the two of them gradually eased open the creaky door. There was the truck and on the walls, hanging from newly driven nails, were two tires. Each took one and back they ran, chased by a barking dog.

Later on, Millard would become less fumbling; he would remember to close garage doors so that it would take a farmer some time to determine what was stolen. This time Millard did not and the farmer, awakened by the dog, called the police, who soon enough found Crook and Millard dispiritedly standing beside the Model-T, wondering what to do with two tires, neither of which fit.

Waiting in the courthouse the next morning, Crook convinced Millard that one and only one of them should assume the blame. Crook was ready to toss for it, but compulsively Millard volunteered. He thought he said "I will" because he didn't care. The truth was that he did care, he cared profoundly that Crook think him bold.

Without a lawyer, Millard heard a judge sentence him to prison for one to two years.

He may not have known it, but he was finally settled into a way of life.

Chapter | 5

Millard entered the Allegheny Workhouse in the sad years when penologists tried to atomize each prisoner, keep him in a spiritual solitary. Prisons in those years deformed men before they rehabilitated them. Millard was assigned to the stamping plant where he worked a machine imprinting license plates, an improvement over the dreadful blank idleness of other prisons. But the men worked in semi-silence, all conversation interdicted. Of course they talked —they worked in groups, they could not help but talk—so work, which filled their day, was always animated by secrecy and guile.

The prison provided no recreation or education. Once a year, on Independence Day, the inmates could mill about the yard, the guards' scrutiny relaxed. It was a futile system. It is hard to reform a man by beating him over the head, although the wardens tried. Then again it is hard for a free man to understand a prisoner. Three men were assigned to a cell to discourage homosexuality. Homosexuality in prisons flourished, and still does, precisely because there are three men in a cell. It is only with three men that two men can bugger each other, for the third is free to signal the guard's approach. Put a man in a cage and he does not always think like a man; he thinks more like an animal. Shame never deters pleasure and men easily dispense with privacy.

Such an atmosphere appalled Millard. He lived now with thieves of all description, alcoholics with no place else to go, dope addicts, derelicts, and homosexuals whom Millard immediately attracted. Benny Jacobs sought him out. Benny was an intelligent safe-cracker, more than usually articulate.

More fascinating was Benny's religious discourse. "I was born a Jew," he said. "My father wore a yarmulke and a long beard and said Kaddish every night. But I couldn't see why we were the Chosen because we didn't eat pork. The Romans ate pork, right? So did the Greeks. It came to me religion was organized superstition."

"You're an atheist?" asked Millard.

"Me and many others," said Benny.

Malcolm Wright despised atheism as other men despised the plague. That someone would embrace it, fearlessly and with some logic, surprised Millard. "Who else?" he pressed.

"Cervantes," said Benny, "Tolstoy, Mark Twain, Victor Hugo, Alexandre Dumas, Balzac."

"Who are they?"

Benny laughed and told him. Benny owned these books. He willingly lent them to Millard. Benny had made a strong appeal. Millard wanted to be an atheist, too.

Millard rather enjoyed being proselytized. He always enjoyed it. Too much. Millard was a would-be proselyte who in his heart knew he would never convert, a proselyte set upon luring the evangelist. He would have had to have been less than naive not to realize straight off Benny was a homosexual. Certainly Millard was interested in atheism, but he flagged Benny past this so that every talk they had became in its way an overture. Encouraging Benny gave Millard a sense of worth, but it was a worth for which he wouldn't pay. He wouldn't bring himself to tell Benny he had no intention of giving as good as he got, for Millard knew that to quell Benny's fervor diminished his own importance.

They sat reading Shakespeare at a barren table in the makeshift library and Benny, leaning forward, said in the prison jargon, "Millard, I want you to be my doll."

Deliberately Millard moved away from him. He stared unblinking at the surprised Benny. Deliberately he closed the book they were discussing and asked coldly, "Is that what you atheists are?"

"But Millard . . ." Benny protested.

Millard stood up. "There are other books I can read," he said scornfully, tossed Shakespeare at Benny's feet, and slowly walked out of the room, without a backward glance.

Benny was a homosexual who could be pleasant or dangerous. He turned dangerous. He told one of the guards Millard had contraband hidden in his mattress—a pencil and writing paper.

The guards ran the usual shakedowns at odd hours. They entered the cells, rummaged through the prisoners' scanty possessions, checked every corner and crevice. Usually the guards punched the pillows, and frisked the mattress to see if the prisoner had secreted a club or a shiv. This time, the guard who entered Millard's cell tossed aside the pillow, removed the muslin cover from the mattress, and quickly extracted the pencil and paper.

Millard knew someone had informed and knew who the someone was—Benny, for Benny had given him the paper and pencil, had even told Millard where to hide them. Contraband meant three days' solitary confinement.

Solitary was in the basement of the east wing of the prison. The inmates called it the "White House." One small bulb, hanging like a raw nerve, barely illuminated the rat-infested cell. The cubicle was furnished only with a wide board, warped from water which seeped continually. The steel door banged. Millard was alone. Within hours he was screaming, scarcely hearing the hollow booming of his voice. Helplessly he surrendered to hallucinations. When the guard opened the slit to pass through the daily ration of bread and water Millard begged him in a harsh, noisy, self-frightening voice to tell him what day it was. The guard kept quiet. Sleep was impossible. Every time Millard felt fatigue relaxing him, he was jolted back to wakefulness by the rats which waited to attack him.

Once again he had maneuvered himself into a position where crushing injustice oppressed him. A pencil and paper! He hated not Benny who had contrived the situation, but the guard who had exploited it. By the end of the third day he was consumed with hatred for the man. Even when he returned to his cell, this hatred grew.

There is little kindness or understanding in prison guards. They are rough men, as rough as the prisoners they control. Their cruelty is at best under fragile control. Millard's guard found his prisoner's quiet provocation intolerable. As if fearing to vent his violence, he grew permissive—and Millard became openly defiant. If there is neither kindness nor understanding in most guards, neither is there a sense of fairness. The guard charged Millard with the possession of a mirror, again contraband. Millard's outrage at so patent an injustice did him no good. Back he went to solitary, strutting into the cell with bravado which gave way to wretched hallucination. This time he was there for five days.

On the fifth day, the guard, troubled by his conscience, asked, "How do you feel? Ready to shape up?"

Millard croaked, "Go to hell!"

The guard, after thumping Millard with his club, pushed and shoved the weak and half-dazed prisoner into the "monkey cage," a barred structure in the prison compound, open to view, too small to accommodate a man prone or supine, too short to accommodate him erect. Millard had to stoop all the while he occupied the cage, a posture which imprinted total submission on his body. After thirty hours, his muscles drained from exhaustion, the pain of his unnatural posture absolute agony, Millard fainted. When he revived, the guards left him for another twenty hours.

Now he had learned, learned how to become a prisoner. He had chosen a way of life and had finally realized that way of life demanded habits and attitudes consonant with it. He was not vindictive. He no longer hated the guard. Millard realized they both had suffered, the guard without conscious pleasure, Millard without conscious malice.

Millard had learned to ask the right question: not "What is society doing to me for stealing two tires?" but "What does prison want from me?" Prison and society are two different places; in the mind of the habitual criminal they are separated forces. A prison is always on guard, a society always unsuspecting. Millard's answer to the question was succinct: prison wanted him to test his capacity to endure. He had proved he could take it. He even liked taking it. He could take more. Punishment could not deter him.

Chapter | 6

He came home that spring of 1928, a young man just over eighteen years old, physically run down, his anger and resentment dimmed into a lackluster pessimism and depression. Malcolm Wright offered him the protected environment, less a home now than simple shelter, a place where Malcolm couldn't hear and Millard wouldn't talk. Malcolm fancied himself one of the rocks against which the stream splits. Millard wasn't even flotsam. He had vegetated along the banks, in stagnant water. It took him several months before the stream began to edge him into its current again.

But it did.

Millard went to a square dance. One of his partners was a redheaded girl who had a Scottish burr and wore dungarees.

Her name was Viola.

"Why do you wear pants?" Millard asked.

"Because I'm a farm girl. Maybe I don't have a dirndl dress. If you don't like honest clothes, you don't have to dance."

"I think you look pretty in dungarees," said Millard. "And I'll bet you're just as pretty in a dirndl dress." He took her arm and led her into the Virginia Reel.

Perhaps that is why he liked her: because she wore dungarees, because she looked like a man, not like a girl, because he sensed she was only to make modest demands upon him. And she liked him for the reasons many women liked him: because he was tall and slim, a breadth under six feet, looking like something strong and masculine out of Texas, except that his shoulders sloped just perceptibly. He wore glasses, which lent him a scholarly mien and his manners and soft voice convinced a woman he was gentle. To women he was somehow remote and distant, like a crescent moon, his angle of approach always obscuring what they hoped was a luminous disc.

"You're not a good dancer," she said.

"I don't have much time for dances," Millard said.

"The busy, busy man," she mocked. "What keeps you so busy?"

"I read," said Millard.

"Why would a man rather read than dance?"

"So he can say nice things to a pretty girl."

"Say something nice," she asked.

"Shall I compare thee to a summer's day? Thou art more temperate. Rough winds do often shake the darling buds of May and summer's lease hath all too short a date."

"Why that's poetry," she said, stopping. "Beautiful."

"It's Shakespeare," said Millard, flushed with his superiority, hoping, too, she wouldn't ask for the conclusion which he hadn't memorized.

"Shakespeare," she exclaimed. "I've heard of him. We read him in school. He's hard. He's an *Englishman*."

It burst from Millard, in a torrent, all the books he'd read, the precise thoughts, the stray paragraphs he had memorized. He couldn't stop himself, not before so willing a listener, not before a listener whose admiration kept ballooning.

"You're practically a professor," she said.

They walked home together. She and her brother, Knox, and his wife, Corinne, worked shares on a large farm. Their hours of toil were long and their livelihood meager.

Viola was a cheery girl, one with a romantic flair. She liked pinning a flower in Millard's lapel and she wanted Millard's praise when she recited the doggerel she herself composed. After a while, he no longer noticed the dungarees and the men's work shirts. She became the playmate he wanted. She wanted no test competitive or sexual. They kissed occasionally, without passion, without real interest, not wanting to prove one was a man and the other a woman, but that they were two souls who needed each other's praise and pleasantness.

Corinne, the sister-in-law, made jokes about their relationship. "You two are stuck on each other," she said. Or, "You two are sugar sweethearts," remarks which faintly embarrassed them. Had Corinne not injected the physical into the companionship— now telling Millard, "Viola is a cuddly girl," now telling Viola, "That Millard looks as strong as a whip," perhaps they wouldn't have kissed at all. Corinne was a voluptuous woman, with freckled, firm arms, a balcony of a bosom, round grapefruits for breasts, and blond hair which she shook often, wanting the sensuous feel of it brushing across her cheek, wanting to know men noticed; she would often fondle her own hips and plunge her hand into her bodice, always asserting the facts of her womanhood. She was a commanding wife, but then she may have had to be. For what family there was, Corinne was the center of gravity. Millard felt an undeniable pull drawing him into a modest but still complete universe.

Millard was not a deadbeat; rather he never thought he was a deadbeat—a man who does not pay his own way. He wanted to join Viola and Corinne and Knox Moon on equal terms. But the ever-punitive society which tirelessly compiles records denied him that chance. He couldn't find a job.

Millard decided upon burglary.

The decision was conceived in passion but it was not rash. Burglary is a passive crime. Though often desperate, it is rarely violent. It offers a covert yet nonetheless satisfying release of tension. In a significant number of instances, the victims or the police will discover the burglar has defecated at the scene of his crime. The burglar has used his feces as an exhibition of defiance. Burglary is a contumacious act, part of a compulsion toward insubordination. Though Millard never indulged in the symbolic act of defecating, his inner mutiny and stubborn refusal to accept authority found adequate expression in rifling homes.

He knew, moreover, a great many of the techniques. Two years in any prison is long enough to make out of any fairly retentive man an expert. Millard knew the risks a cat burglar ran and he knew how to minimize those risks. A cat burglar robs occupied homes. Entering, a cat burglar immediately turns up the thermostat one or two degrees. The muffled boom of the igniting oil burner usually lulls the occupants' instinctive vigilance and excuses inadvertent noises the burglar makes. Women always leave their purses in the kitchen and men always leave their wallets and their watches on the night table. A woman will deposit her house money in an obvious kitchen bowl and a man will often keep extra money in his bank book in his desk. Jewelry is invariably in a box in the top drawer of a bureau.

Less risky, of course, is burglarizing an empty house. It is simple to determine which house lacks occupants. Millard would walk the streets at that time in the late afternoon or early evening when lights begin to fill the downstairs windows. Sauntering until the real dark descended, seeing which windows stayed dark, he would prepare. Getting inside was never a problem. There wasn't a locked window Millard couldn't open. He would put his hands on the frame and gently, but with all his might, push the window frame to the left and then push straight down, release it, push it to the left again and then again hard down. Sooner or later the window would work its way free from the catch since wood and even metal give under this pressure.

He often resorted to windows since back doors are not always on the dark side of the house. When back doors were in blackness, entry was easy. People leave the key, when they bother to lock the back door at all, under mats, inside milk boxes, on the lintel, and frequently under the stone beneath the drain pipe. If Millard couldn't find the key, he opened a square bolt in the same manner he opened a window; a strip of celluloid opened a door with a beveled latch or undid an interior hook. Determined pressure will break a chain guard or wrench a double bolt from the frame and any burglar can kick in a door.

Millard could throw a golf ball through the window, undo the latch, steal only cash and jewelry, and depart. He would leave the golf ball behind, knowing that when the owners returned, they would presume immediately that some careless boy had driven it through the glass. Rarely would they bother to check their possessions.

He never carried gloves in the summer. Gloves are incriminating evidence to any policeman, just as sneakers are incriminating. Millard masked his fingerprints by wrapping handkerchiefs around his hands. He prowled in his stocking feet.

Not even vicious dogs would frighten him off. The way to calm a growling dog is to lead him to the kitchen and feed him. In fact, as an ironic gesture, Millard once calmed and stole a German shepherd. On another occasion, when he was recounting the number of homes he had robbed, he discovered the police discounted one of the robberies because of the presence of a trained police dog.

"It was too me," Millard protested.

"Naw," said the officer, "that was an inside job."

"I remember that dog," Millard said. "He ran into the room and jumped up on the bed with his muddy paws."

Burglars are notorious braggarts and Millard was no exception. They have memories which catalog precisely what they stole. They are infinitely more accurate than the owners. Later in his career, when one owner charged Millard with stealing, among other things, three bottles of imported Scotch, Millard indignantly told the police, "It was not imported Scotch. It was two bottles of A & P wine."

Millard rarely chose the risky jobs. For the most, he always entered empty homes and almost invariably stole things rather than money. He would make his way to the bedroom closet where he usually found the family's suitcases, then he would fill these with whatever caught his fancy. Burglary was always another way of taking a journey to Millard. There was no consistency in the things he stole. Though he was bright enough, he made careless and disorderly plans. His thought was episodic because he thought in scenes, rarely in terms of goals. He had a complete knowledge of burglary and a technical expertise. But with all that, he was occasionally inept: He would forget to bring a nail file to jimmy open a locked suitcase or he couldn't remember where he had placed his shoes or sometimes he would flee at unexplained sounds, leaving the thefts behind.

All burglars are inept, for all of them sooner or later serve prison sentences. While burglars have well-developed instincts, they fail to realize the police have instincts every bit as developed. The police, in fact, have a wider and longer experience, for their profession is never interrupted by jail terms. A burglar who goes in a window and out a door will always go in a window and out a door, a *modus operandi* which immediately informs the police whether a series of robberies is the work of one thief or two thieves or several. A burglar will always rob the same kind of house in the same kind of neighborhood because he knows pretty well what that house usually contains. This alerts the police to the types of goods he has probably stolen. It is a protracted but not complicated process to question all the neighbors as to whom they saw at a certain hour on a certain evening. Invariably someone remembers a suspicious figure. It is a tedious business to post policemen at intersections to keep track of the passing autos and pedestrians, to check out the odd car or walker, but in a large number of cases this is the way the police and the burglar cross paths. It takes skill and patience to follow a suspect. Often, however, the suspect will lead the police to the house he robs.

Few burglars could operate without pawnshops. But pawnbrokers are no fools. They keep extensive files, all of them cross-indexed. One entry lists name and address, another a detailed description of items pawned, another the date. By checking these indexes, the police were able to arrest Millard in 1928.

They let him stew a while this time, thinking over the clumsy story he'd told. Then they questioned him politely, coaxing, ever persuading.

Millard kept insisting it was a mistake. He'd found that suitcase with the fur coats in it, he was only going to hock them to get the money to help his father with the mortgage. It hurt that he was draining his father; you see, he was out of work. No, he never stole anything.

One of the policemen offered him a pack of cigarettes and a book of matches. Millard lit up.

"What did you pull time for?" asked the detective.

"What makes you think I pulled time?" asked Millard.

"You split the match when you lit your cigarette. You can always get cigarettes in the big house, but you can't get matches.

Millard Wright before the lobotomy (about thirty years old).

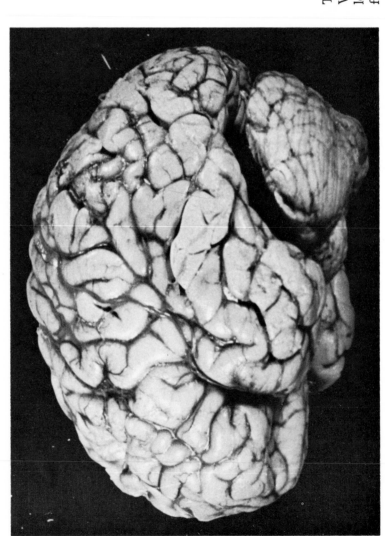

The left side of Millard Wright's brain. The lobotomy scar is seen in the frontal area.

Diagrammatic representation of cortical localization of function and area of incision for frontal lobotomy.

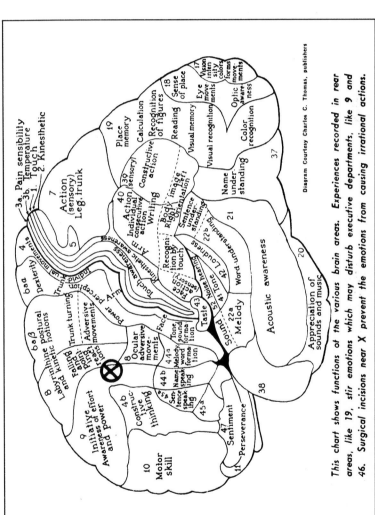

This chart shows functions of the various brain areas. Experiences recorded in rear areas, like 19, stir emotions which may disturb executive departments, like 9 and 46. Surgical incisions near X prevent the emotions from causing irrational actions.

Diagram Courtesy Charles C. Thomas, publishers

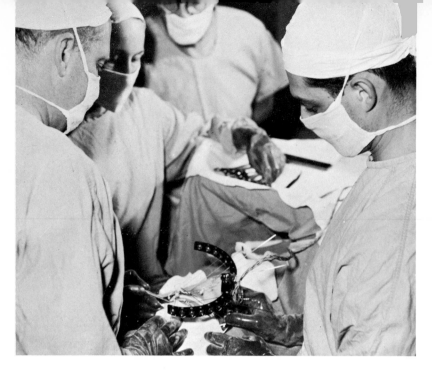

Neurosurgical operation upon Millard Wright for implantation of intra-cerebral electrodes (Dr. Yale David Koskoff is at left). CREDIT: *Monte-fiore Hospital*

X ray of Wright's skull depicting probe to the edge of lesser wing of sphenoid. The lobotomy was carried out along this line.

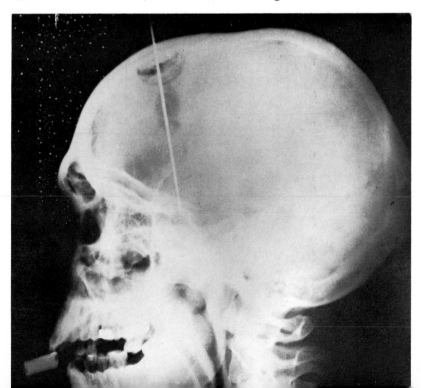

I never saw a con didn't split his matches. You going to tell us what you went for? Or are we going to have to waste time looking it up?"

"Burglary," said Millard softly. The story tumbled out. Dates, addresses, disposal, the police stenographer writing it all down as Millard itemized everything, object by object.

So six months after he had been released, another judge sent Millard Wright back to the Allegheny County Workhouse. This time, Millard knew more. Just as he knew more about how to rob homes, so he knew how to deal with the law and the courts. He knew the difference between breaking and entering, which is a daylight robbery, and burglary, which is a nighttime offense, and consequently merits a heavier penalty—a distinction which existed in Pennsylvania law until 1939. He knew a prosecuting attorney would ask, "Want to save the county time and money? Want to save yourself some anguish? A guilty plea to breaking and entering will get you two to four, which means you'll do a year."

Millard shuffled up before a judge and mumbled, "Guilty." He purposely kept his head down, his body motionless. He looked seedy and he looked defeated. Millard could pose as that anonymous figure, that shabby parcel of unregenerate humanity, who knows only a pale identity. He was another mindless wretch a judge dispatched to prison, the judge stifling a yawn as the bailiff called the next case.

This was not the first time the police had caught him. But that does not mean Millard was without cunning. He was cunning, for it takes a certain cunning for a man to realize when he's caught. It takes cunning to make the best of prison, cunning and manipulative abilities.

Within days after he had arrived at the Workhouse, Millard reported to the prison doctor. He complained of short breath, immense fatigue, recurring chest pains.

"You might have heart trouble," said the doctor. "Do you have any history of cardiac disease?"

Millard had no cardiac problem. But he knew the symptoms and its history because Edith had been a heart patient for many years.

The doctor was concerned: Yes, Millard was cunning, he never relaxed. He dragged himself to his workbench, he breathed heavily at night, awakening himself to feign annoying moans. Soon enough, the young doctor made his diagnosis: Millard's heart was failing. Prison doctors had little more than stethoscopes and aspirin for equipment. They dealt primarily with a variety of venereal diseases, admixed with degenerative disease induced by alcoholism and malnutrition. This young doctor was sure he saw in Millard a textbook illustration, the classic manifestation of heart disease.

Millard instructed his sister Lillian. She petitioned a circuit court judge for leniency. Viola Moon supported Lillian's plea. The doctor filed a deposition, stating this young man could only worsen in prison. In all, it took ten months, ten months of disciplined faking, ten months of controlled never-ending pretense before the doctor, the courts, and the other prisoners. A judge, mindful of the State's responsibility, released Millard on probation to die or convalesce at home.

"Free again," said Malcolm when he saw his son. "Free to steal."

"Not this time," said Millard. "This time I might get married."

"Some knight in shining armor," grunted Malcolm.

That is curiously what Millard thought he was. He was a knight in shining armor who took risks, who remained true to a pointless oath, who never swore nor treated a woman crudely nor took physical advantage of her, a man who worshiped his maid from afar, chasing that ideal as knights futilely pursued the Grail. He was a figure of gentle yet heroic proportions. Indeed, as far as knights go, Millard was one: He was as delinquent as any of the knights of the Round Table, for certainly they weren't slaying dragons; there are no dragons. They were slaying people, robbing and pillaging, and then romanticizing their delinquent behavior. Millard putting one foot after another over a windowsill was in the same heroic mold as Launcelot, who venerated chastity yet desecrated it as soon as desire swelled within him. Millard's code was equally as complex and rigid as Launcelot's and equally antisocial and self-punishing.

Chapter | 7

Malcolm had long ago surrendered the expectation Millard would prove a good son. He paid for Millard's new clothes and he urged him to find work and he fed him, but these were mechanical efforts. Millard was just a physical presence, an indifferent presence who claimed food and lodging from time to time, which Malcolm provided not out of a grudging admission that he was, after all, the father, but out of habit.

They lived together never wanting communication or love or friendship or pity or respect. Millard didn't even bother to confide to his father that he could not find work in the area.

But Millard did tell Viola. "Everyone knows about me," he said. "I can't find a job. No one will trust me. I'd be better off back in prison."

"Yes, you can get a job," said Viola. "You can go some place else. You can go to Cleveland."

"What's in Cleveland?" Millard asked dispiritedly.

"Corinne and Knox moved to Cleveland. They say there's a lot of work there. You can live with them. They bought a boarding-house and maybe Knox knows someone where he works."

"But I'll be in Cleveland and you'll be here. What good is that?"

"My mother and I are going to Cleveland next summer. That's not so long away. Maybe you'll be all settled by then."

Borrowing money from Viola, Millard went to Cleveland. Knox Moon told him Madison Steel was taking on men. He applied there and was hired. He said he was a riveter. He had never held a riveting jack; he didn't realize he had to trail the air hose over his right shoulder; nor did he know how to control the pressure. Now he had to maneuver. But prison had made him adept. He was clever enough to realize that there are few jobs a man cannot learn and command simply by asking his fellow workers how to do them. Most of us who conform live with an ethic which preaches what we ought to be: Millard lived with the criminal's ethic which told him what he could be. Millard wasn't any more successful with his ethic than most of us are with ours but his ethic was often pragmatic. Between the other riveters and his helper, Millard soon was proficient enough to earn his pay.

As Viola had promised, Corinne and Knox Moon took him in. The boardinghouse they owned was one of those cumbersome frame dwellings in a Cleveland factory district, the windows clouded by smoke, made rough with grit. Inside there was the bare minimum of pretension. Two of the floors were covered by Axminister rugs which, their borders filled with flowers, copied Oriental and Persian carpeting. The murky brown mohair chairs showed bald on back and cushion but their threadbare arms were covered with soiled antimacassars. Under each table lamp was a grimy doily. The walls were stippled and lined by little valleys of dust. Black imitation-ivory elephants forever plodded across a bookcase partially filled with *True Confessions, Real Life Stories, Liberty Magazine,* and *Silver Screen,* all stacked sideways.

Corinne, the wellspring of the family, made Millard welcome. Her brother, John Araway, and her husband, Knox, accepted without demurrer the values Corinne assigned. They were working men, accustomed to think of themselves as the recipients of the forces and accidents of life, never the controllers. Their gossip was as stale as their minds. They refused to believe their senses which should have convinced them Corinne was intent on seducing Millard. They blinded themselves to this perhaps because Millard did too. Millard blinded himself not because he didn't

understand what Corinne wanted but because he didn't understand why.

Yet it was there. There were sly winks and frequently Corinne
put her hand on him during casual conversations, even when the
other men were present. Her eyes widened and her generous
mouth smiled as soon as Millard walked into the house. Invariably she laid aside a household chore to come near him and laugh
or sympathize about the events of the day.

She was four years Millard's senior, twenty-five, a more than
attractive woman and a more than flirtatious one, too.

Millard didn't discourage her. He led her on. Before he went
to work, he always helped her wash the breakfast dishes and
make the beds. But he never matched the ardor of her advances.
It was she who put his hand on her breast, she who kissed his neck
and ear, she who fondled him. He never pulled away from her,
never resisted in embarrassment or stern modesty. He only expressed amazement. Corinne, like Potiphar's wife, kept pursuing.
Millard played Joseph. His reluctance was a coaxing. One week
passed into the next and the minuet grew more complicated but
remained as delicate.

"Oh, Millard, kiss me!" she breathed.

"What about Knox? What about Viola?"

"Kiss me, kiss me."

She had asked for the kiss. His giving, he rationalized, did not
despoil him. He wouldn't satisfy her, but he didn't keep from
promising satisfaction. She became bolder, more daring. When
they had finished tucking in a sheet one morning, she crawled
over the bed on her knees to his side and determinedly pulled him
to a sitting position next to her. She bared her bosom, pressed his
face against it. She took his hand and placed it against her soft
mons and squeezed her thighs together. "Get in there, you bas-
tard, and *dig!*" she said.

"What?" asked Millard, finally extricating himself.

"Bite," she said, and pushed his head against her bosom.

"Here? On this bed?" he asked.

"I want a man to muss me. Knox doesn't treat me right. Take
me, take me now." She writhed and moaned. Millard, afraid of

the consequences, afraid of himself, and truly afraid of her, pulled free.

Late in the summer, Viola and her mother, Augusta Moon, arrived in Cleveland. Millard had never really known his own mother, let alone a mother about to become his mother-in-law. It proved a traumatic experience. Augusta was a woman who had suffered through a hard childhood and a long courtship, suffered childbirth, suffered a selfish ne'er-do-well husband, and suffered daughters who married beneath them. Augusta never finished dinner that she didn't suffer gastric pains, never went to bed that she didn't suffer insomnia, never sat in a chair that she didn't suffer from the draft.

When Augusta met Millard she barked, "If you're going to marry my daughter Viola, why are you making her go to work?"

"I don't want her to work," Millard answered.

"Well, she's got a job at the cosmetic counter in the five-and-ten. Had the job before she came here. Thought it was odd for an engaged lady, but decided to hold my peace till I saw her fiancé."

"Viola, if we're to get married, I don't want you working."

"I've always worked," said Viola.

"But I don't want it," said Millard, trying his level best to sound stern.

"Then don't marry me," she said.

Millard acceded. He wanted to get married just as Viola wanted to get married, not because they were in love, nor because they thought it was better to marry than to burn, nor because they wanted the security of a white house with a rose-covered picket fence, although they pretended this was what they wanted; no, they wanted to marry because that was what people did: They got married in the same way they went to school, because society ordered and forced them.

Corinne brought their disagreement into the family dialogue. John and Knox and Corinne and Millard and Viola and the dogmatic Augusta kept offering their irresolute opinions as to whether or not Viola should work. When Viola one evening let her boss escort her home, Millard stamped from the dining room in a sulk, ready to abandon marriage, forgetting the girl had grown while he was in jail, forgetting that the mere fact he had chosen her was no guarantee she was faithful.

The newlyweds stayed on at Corinne's. But the bliss Millard expected was short-lived. Augusta told him, "I didn't think much of you when Viola told me you had been in the county work-house. Now I think less. Any man that would let his wife go to work when he has his own job isn't cut out to be much."

Night after night, the same criticism came at Millard over the same crocheted table cloth. Night after night Millard fumbled with the same ragged magazines as he tried nervously to explain.

One day a few months after his marriage, Millard was ill. He begged off work and came home early. As he approached the house, he saw a parked car. It struck him as odd that the rumble seat was up and the curtains down. He started up the front walk when a girlish laugh from the car turned him back. He wrenched open the door. There in the front seat, her skirt pulled into her lap, her blouse open and her cheeks aflame sat Viola, another man's arms around her.

Millard slammed the door. He ran into the house.

"You're home early," said Augusta.

"And about time," snapped Millard. "You," he sneered. "A mother. Want to see the kind of mother you are. Look." He pulled the old woman to him, pushed apart the curtains on the front door window and made Augusta watch as Viola, still straightening her clothes, stepped from the car.

Roughly he released Augusta and after stamping up the stairs, set to packing his battered suitcase. He heard Viola come in and exchange whispers with her mother. "Let her come to me," he thought as he continued his frenzied packing. "Nothing like this ever happened to the Wrights," he told himself.

A week later she found him through his sister, and he went back. He had waited, imagining all the while the recriminations and criticisms the family spat at Viola. He found as soon as he entered the house, they hadn't discussed him at all. They talked to him as though he had never been away.

One night he asked Viola to go to the movies with him. She told him she wasn't feeling well. "You go," she said. "Do you good to get away from Mother."

He walked to the drugstore, stopped and sipped a chocolate ice-cream soda. He decided he could forgive his wife. She did think of him. Perhaps it wasn't fair for him to enjoy himself while she lay home with a sick headache. He should be by her, comforting her, making little plans. He went home.

Outside the house, he saw the car again. There was Viola about to get into it. She froze on the running board as she saw him, her hand still daintily lifting her skirts. Before he could move, she stepped back from the running board to the sidewalk, turned, and ran. Millard started chasing her, but came to a halt as he saw the man, vainly reaching over from the driver's side to slam the car door shut. They stared at each other with a strange curiosity.

Then Millard said, "I'm her brother."

"You're Knox?" said the man, relaxing. "You Knox, sure enough? She took off so scared I thought she saw her husband."

"I'm Knox Moon," Millard said, resting his arm on the coupe's roof. "And you shouldn't be out with her. She's a married woman."

"Yeah, I know. But I'm her boss and we've got a yen for each other. What the hell, we see each other every day. And I know what the poor kid's going through."

"With her mother?"

"With that husband the mother made her marry. With that Millard, the ex-con. He beats her. Which is something I'd like to stop and *you* ought to," he said, pointing his finger at Millard.

"Beats her?"

"Beats her and I'll tell you something else. He won't take care of her either. Now I hope you don't take offense at this, but I've had to take care of her now and then. Sexually, you know. The poor kid is desperate. I know this is not the kind of talk the boyfriend exchanges with the brother, but, really, the family ought to do something about that Millard. What are you? Cowards?"

"I'll tell you what I am," said Millard. "I'm her husband. I'm Millard, the ex-con. And you're an adulterer, a man who breaks the sixth commandment."

Millard flung the car door shut and started toward the house, hearing the car roar off before he reached the stoop.

Viola had slipped into Corinne's room where she cried all

night after locking the door. She worried that Millard would beat her, that he would leave her, that he would scorn her. Stroking Viola's hair, Corinne promised to talk to Millard, to make him forgive. Alone in his room, Millard put his head in his pillow and he cried as he never cried when his father had beaten him, when the police had roughly treated him, when the jailers had put him in solitary—he knew what to expect from fathers, policemen, and jailers.

He left the next morning, carrying his meager belongings in his cardboard suitcase, acutely conscious of the pity he deserved.

He would have taken Viola back if she had asked. She didn't have to. She had only to show up at his boardinghouse two weeks later and tell him, "I'm going to have a baby. You know it's yours. Take me back and I'll be a good girl."

She told him this while he sat staring hard-eyed at her, leaning against the brass bedpost, making her confess, savoring her repentance. The prospect of a child suddenly thrilled and excited him. He reached out his arms and took Viola into them. She had asked him once when he refused love, "What the hell are you?" And it had hurt because he didn't know what the hell he was—man, woman, or monk. A baby! Now he knew.

They talked. She would bear that baby and when it came into this world Millard would protect it. That night, at least, they believed each other. Millard came back home with her to the interminable dinner-table gossip and advice. They told him he ought to call the baby Howard if it was a boy, after Viola's father, or Anne if it was a girl, after the grandmother.

"I want to call the baby Malcolm, after my father," Millard protested.

"There will be other babies," said Knox, winking, and Millard blushed.

Augusta took no part in this. Millard mistakenly supposed that the pregnancy had convinced her Viola was at last a woman, her husband's wife, not her mother's daughter. He guessed wrongly. Augusta had found the abortionist.

A few days later, wan and pale, hardly moving, Viola told him about it when he came back from work. She said, "Mother's right. We really shouldn't have children now. We should wait. You are just out of jail. It would be unfair to a baby." He never knew whether the explosion which sent him off on a burglary spree through three states was one of relief over what Viola had done or one of despair. Certainly the abortion took something from him, and drove him to take from others. He had been deprived before and punished for taking things not his own. He had never had anything his own really, except a wife which now he knew he would have to share with others. He had thought the child would be really his. Maybe he would have made a go of life as a father, but Augusta, that stern societal menace, and Viola, that pliant demi-girl, left him again abandoned.

Chapter | 8

The spree came to an end in Cleveland, the city to which he returned after burglarizing several towns in Pennsylvania, West Virginia, and Ohio. It came to an ignominious end without the collusion of pawnbrokers, without clever detection, without policemen passing money to a greedy stool pigeon. It ended when Millard, having rifled a home, lit a match to find his way out when his flashlight died.

Two policemen on their way to work saw the brief flare before Millard cradled it. They stopped, looked at each other, waited and fell in beside Millard as he hurried around from the back across the lawn, lugging two suitcases to the sidewalk.

"We'll just keep right on," said one policeman taking Millard's arm. "The precinct house is only three blocks away." In the station house, when police opened the suitcases, they found watches, rings, clothing, jewelry, and a German Luger.

"And where were you going?" they asked.

"I was on my way to the bus depot. I was going to take a little vacation," said Millard.

"With a Luger?"

"In case," said Millard lamely.

"And where were you going to wear the woman's fur?"

Millard shrugged.

"You're going to like your accommodations," said the policeman. "No tipping. Turkey twice a year. Restricted clientele."

The policeman latched shut the suitcases. "State Exhibit Number One. Since you're Exhibit Number Two, we'll start off with your name."

"Millard Wright," he answered.

"Don't give me that," said the policeman cuffing him. "Give me your name."

"Millard Wright," he offered again, this time in amazement.

The open palm slammed across his ear. "Try again."

Millard held to the chair now to keep from falling. "I can't tell you anything but what it is. My name is Millard Wright."

The other policeman hit him across the mouth, loosening a tooth. "I suppose you're going to tell you haven't been robbing those downtown hotels?"

"That's everything I ever took," said Millard, "what's in the suitcase."

His eyes were blackened, the front of his shirt was drenched with blood, and his head rang with pain before he said in desperation, "My name is John Livengood."

"That's better," they said, ceasing, the sweat rolling from them. "Much better." They led him out and booked him under the name of John Livengood, the name of his sister Edith's husband, whom he hadn't seen in years.

In the morning, gently exploring his cut lips and kneading the bumps along his head, Millard realized the police had simply elected him as the suspect they were seeking. They were not hard reasons for Millard to fathom. He had been around policemen enough to know they were often high-handed. The hotel robber, whoever he was, was what other burglars call a "fogger"—in with the fog, they said, and out with the fog and no one the wiser. But the public didn't know, nor the newspapers, nor the district attorney that this fogger was gone. And the public and the press and the D.A. would keep hammering for the robber's apprehension. The police obliged. They produced a hotel robber. He couldn't be Millard Wright because Millard Wright had never robbed a hotel in his life. Millard Wright, they already knew, was a reform-school punk. They wanted a John Livengood who had no criminal record.

But it wasn't all to the policemen's advantage. John Livengood was a first offender which meant a lighter sentence. It also meant the jewels and valuables Millard Wright had stored in a railroad checkroom were his for the police couldn't very well insist Millard reveal this cache, since none of these valuables had been stolen from any Cleveland hotel. Millard could pawn or fence them, hire a good lawyer, post bail, perhaps skip if his lawyer said the case was hopeless.

When the lawyer asked directly about his fee, Millard whispered, "I had a room in the YMCA, 913. In my drawer there, you'll find four starched shirts. Pasted on the back of the cardboard in the blue shirt, you'll find a checkroom stub. Claim it from the railroad station. There ought to be three or four thousand dollars in rings and necklaces and jewels. How's that for a starter?"

"Might even be enough," said the lawyer.

What Millard didn't realize was that if shady policemen and furtive criminals can talk out of the corner of their mouths so can shifty lawyers. This lawyer claimed the goods, pawned them, and vanished.

A judge sentenced twenty-one-year old Millard Wright to from one to fifteen years in the Ohio State Reformatory. Once again a deputy transported him to a forbidding prison, led him to the front gate before unlocking the handcuffs, and said, "So long," the gratuitous remark to which Millard never responded. Once again he walked across a hard-packed prison yard on his way to a lukewarm shower, an ill-fitting uniform, and a cell barren except for a washbowl, toilet, and canvas cot.

The Ohio Reformatory was a pentagonal structure; on the north and east were three walls of thick, damp stone; on the south and west, past which the deep Kokosing River curved, were two stockade wooden walls. On all five corners were towers which housed revolving spotlights.

Prisons all looked alike to him because prison is numbers. A prisoner wears a number and he answers to that number, rarely to his name. He serves a certain number of years in the company of others all of whom resemble him. Within the month, Millard, like all the prisoners, would know without counting the number of steps it took him from his cell door to his positioned place in line; he knew the number of steps it took to march along the balcony cell block, down the spiral staircase, across the exercise area to the mess hall; the number of steps from his table to the garbage cans; and from the garbage cans to the workshops. He would anticipate these numbers day after day and month after month until the numbers became more monotonous than the action itself. Prison is the number of passages a guard makes every night, occasionally banging his club along the bars, awakening the sleeping. These numbers parade endlessly through the prisoner's head; they become not only his metaphysic but his ethic, too. Time is divided into numbers, not into seasonal passage. Days and nights or a warm spell or a blizzard are finite; and the prisoner lives in terms of the infinite. Time is his implacable enemy. Infinity, that condition in which the last number is no nearer the end than the first is the way a prisoner understands his enemy. Prisoners are always counting, subconsciously or consciously, reciting over and over the numbers which revolve through their memories like stars through the heavens.

Prisons always look and feel and smell alike because the society which acts within is as artificial as the numbers. It is a classless society with neither property nor privilege, with little chance for preference. The work never varies nor does the food. Yet still it is capricious. In a society absolutely determined by exterior forces, every interior member believes he belongs to the aristocracy. There are those who are innocent, those who deserve acquittal, those who are cunning, those who are smart, those who are rebellious, those who are strong, those who lead, and those who are loners—and each of these is a supposed elite so that every prisoner lives with an ever-enlarging sense of status. If he is a lawyer either by profession or study, he can direct an appeal through the courts from his cell, which makes other prisoners defer to him; if he is a burglar, he prides himself on his nerves and resourcefulness; if he is a lifer, his experience has taught him the ins and outs of the prison routine; if he is young, he is desired by the homosexuals; if he succumbs to their blandishments, in time when he becomes old, he is able to seduce the other young "cherries." The prisoner often considers himself a leader by virtue of his ability to "con" the guards—and he will always use the word "con" rather than the more precise verb "fool" because "fool" is a child's word.

As a rookie—as John Livengood—Millard attended school half a day. The prison school had nine grades and while Millard could read with proficiency, he could barely add and subtract. Captain Clayton Worley, who superintended all the prisoners, assigned Millard to the eighth grade. Worley had been a Marine master sergeant for fourteen years until World War I. Commissioned as an officer, he had lost his leg in the Argonne. Discharged, he picked up a career as a prison supervisor. Not particularly a sensitive man, he did appreciate discipline and obedience. Millard was his best student, the most disciplined and the most obedient. Worley was sentimental. In his time, he had coached several men who entered the Naval Academy from the ranks. Again he had an eager student. He supplied the prison library with Shakespeare because Millard had requested it and he even added copies of Nietzsche and Schopenhauer. Millard was conning him; Millard didn't know the difference between an ethic and a metaphysic but neither did Worley. Millard was conning really because Worley's interest flattered him. Although Millard had an unsystematic mind, it wasn't long before he realized he read Shakespeare and biographies when his mood was expectant and Nietzsche and Schopenhauer when he was depressed.

Reading in prison is always accompanied by annoyance since a simple-minded guard, hurriedly scanning each page of a book, will always clip out any passage he thinks relates to sex, insubordination, or crime. Which meant Millard would often turn from page 14 to page 67. Letters from wives, mothers, sisters, brothers, and lovers were also often interrupted by an impatient pair of scissors. Millard, however, couldn't write to his wife, Viola, or to Corinne, whom he knew would answer, or to his father. He was John Livengood and he had to remain John Livengood. He told a departing cellmate about the disguise. "Will you get in touch with Viola?" he asked.

"Sure," the cellmate agreed.

Millard never heard from Viola because the cellmate told Viola Millard had syphilis. Years later, in another prison, Millard met the man again and accosted him.

"Why would you tell that woman such a thing? I never had syphilis in my life."

The man shrugged. "I spent eight years in Ohio and I got out wanting a woman. I figured if I told her that, she'd screw me out of being mad at you. And she did. And I'll tell you now, all the time you spent there, you weren't missing nothing. See, it all proves one thing—never give any son-of-a-bitch an advantage."

Millard was not particularly interested in prison's forbidden pleasures—alcohol, sex, or gambling. But during this term, what did interest him was the prison newspaper which the convicts themselves edited and published. When the editor of the paper sought Millard out and asked for a composition, Millard eagerly complied. He became a frequent columnist, writing about literature and the need for a prison school. He was delighted to see his name in print but even here he was manipulative. Fame in prison is hard to come by but a prison reporter is famous among the other inmates. Yet even this fame wasn't enough for Millard. He contributed to the paper partly to satisfy his ego and partly to convince the prison administration to assign him to the printing plant, where the work was easier, varied, and more interesting. After a year and a half Captain Worley summoned him to the prison office and congratulated him on his behavior.

"I think you've changed, Livengood," said Worley. "I think you've made the best of it. I am transferring you to one of the honor cottages outside the wall. I want you to keep up the good work and if you do, you'll shorten your time."

The honor cottages were on the far side of the Kokosing and in the spring and summer, the trees shielded the view of the forbidding stockade. The honor prisoners did farm work under a competent and fair administrator. Their morale was excellent and they were allowed privacy every evening and could furnish their cottages with small necessities. Millard had discovered the little blue books published by E. Haldeman-Julius and stuffed his work pants with these miniature volumes, reading them through his noon break and through every rest period.

Still, he played a role. He knew the prisoner who reads is the rare one. That prisoner does not come under the scrutiny of the guards as much as he comes under their wonder. And the wonder of a guard is a valuable thing to a man penned-up. For that wonder can mean relaxation, a shortening of time, a certain ease. Within months, Captain Worley made Millard an Inmate Officer, a luxurious privilege. Millard served as an auxiliary guard. A stern discipline warned other prisoners off.

The assignment frightened Millard; more, it appalled him. The other prisoners called the Inmate Guards "finks." They were renegades and the Inmate Guards knew it as they also knew any infraction on their part put them back into this population, into terrors only prisoners know how to inflict. Yet how could you refuse an assignment from a man who held your time in his hands, whose desultory mark upon a chart could represent months and years of restraint and surveillance? Millard really preferred the security of sustained authority and the relief of punishment. But the role he constantly played compelled him to say yes to Worley. To deny he wanted release was to become what the other prisoners called a "waterhead," a man so inured to prison, he could no longer adapt to the world outside.

In blue dungarees and a faded blue workshirt, a billy club dangling from his belt, Millard patrolled the catwalk on the wooden stockade. He answered now to his name, not his number. It went well enough at first. He paced from sundown until dawn, escaping the malevolent stares of the other convicts, the day to himself, the nights uneventful.

Then came one overcast night. There was no moon.

Suddenly sirens shrieked. The main gates clanged shut. The guards shouted orders which the wind and the night confused.

Millard heard the machine gun in the booth swivel, heard the ammunition belt clip in. Searchlights erratically mowed the ground, the walls, the bright globes intersecting each other, bouncing off corners, circling wildly as their glare sought to encapsule the prisoners.

Below, suddenly, Millard heard it—a makeshift pick digging into the wood on the wall. Of course! The river side. A body, coursing and lunging up the rope, panting, "Livengood, give us a hand." Prisoners trying to leap past his station into the river.

Without the barest consideration, Millard loosened the pick.

With a shocked yell, the prisoner below fell back to the ground and Millard beat a tattoo on the wood with his club, signaling for lights and guards. Quickly, the spotlights concentrated on the two confused men below who, panic-stricken, dashed first to the right, then to the left as a posse of guards rushed upon them. A guard brought his club down twice and the escaping prisoners wrapped their arms around their heads in submission. The guards dragged them to the prison, their arms bound now, one of the men sobbing, the other stumbling behind, bleeding badly. Then and only then, when the night sealed off the compound below, did Millard wonder who inside had seen? Who inside would know? What would those inside do?

"You're going to get out of here, Livengood," hissed an inmate the next day. "In a garbage can. In bits and pieces."

Captain Worley sent for him. "Of course, I heard," he said to Millard. "They know it was you. And I know what that means. So I'm going to do more than transfer you back to the honor cottages, Livengood. I'm going to recommend you for parole, immediate parole. You've become what I knew you could become, a model prisoner, a man who gets a second chance."

The chairman of the parole board asked, "Livengood, whom do you think will act as your sponsor if we grant this release now?"

Millard answered automatically, "Millard Wright, in Black Lick, Pennsylvania."

The board approved his parole that morning. By noon he was on a bus, headed toward Pittsburgh. Millard had served less than two years of a sentence which might have stretched to fifteen. Reading over his parole papers he admired his own cunning. The parole board had made him his own guardian. Millard Wright didn't have to report to a parole supervisor, John Livengood did. The thing to do was get rid of John. Deliberately Millard tore the papers into small pieces and threw them out the bus window, not stopping to consider in his defiance he had indeed become what they wanted, a model prisoner but a model prisoner with this difference: he was a model prisoner predetermined to go back, a waterhead. He was the model prisoner who finds life viable not in the possession of an identity, which Millard had recently discovered was for him a simple convenience, but in participating in the routine and regularity of a systematized society. Millard wanted that which he had come every day to expect, not that over which he had daily to exercise choice, if not will.

Had he opted for honest work, for choice, for will, Black Lick couldn't have helped him in the late summer of 1931. The Depression was on and the Depression ravaged the rural and agricultural communities more brutally than it ravaged the large cities. Already, idle men, young and old, collected on the street corners in Black Lick, aimlessly considering the blank days and weeks ahead. Already the housewives chipped in their pennies for one of their number to buy a cake of soap they could all divide. Smoke no longer belched from the factory chimneys, and women knew hard times were here because their window curtains stayed clean. The stores were boarded up. There was no job for any young man even if he did not have a criminal record.

Chapter | 9

Millard, of course, thought he had a profession to which he could turn. He was a professional criminal.

By the summer of 1931, black, bold headlines in seventy-two point, described the successes of other professional criminals—the Dillingers, the Baby Face Nelsons, the Pretty Boy Floyds, the desperadoes who had adapted the car to urban crime. They flourished and flourished adventurously, becoming a national issue in the early 1930's.

Because they were infamous Millard tried to emulate them. But he wasn't a proficient professional criminal. He wasn't a proficient criminal anymore than Pretty Boy Floyd, Baby Face Nelson, and Dillinger were. They knew their robberies, kidnapings, murders, bank holdups were intermittent events between prison terms. They spent their money on quack surgeons who smashed their cheekbones to change their faces and seared their hands to change fingerprints. But this didn't make them professional criminals because professional criminals know where the easy money is. The professional criminals had already infiltrated the labor unions; they were already, in 1931, shucking the apparatus of bootlegging; they had discovered there was more money in policy numbers day after day, in nickles and dimes, than there was in all of the banks and loan companies of urban America. The professional criminal was a professional by virtue of his ability to avoid imprisonment.

Millard had no chance of avoiding imprisonment. He was a simple American victimized by the idea that the automobile could organize the whole of life. He never comprehended the painstaking care total organization had to have. He recruited six of those men of the street corners, none so corrupt as they were desperate, none so dangerous as they were amateurish, and with these amateurs, Millard robbed several homes, making enough money to buy a rumble-seat Ford car. Then he began to mastermind daring robbery raids afar, masterminding them to the extent he pointed to a town on a well-creased road map and led the expedition to it. Millard was a mastermind because he procured the gasoline, because he taught his skills, because he carried a .38 Colt automatic and a blackjack. It was a role. Millard knew it was a role carried on to impress the amateurs. No competent burglar ever carries a gun since the police stop a known burglar too often and too casually. A salt cellar in a sock is as effective as any manufactured blackjack.

In his new car, the rumble seat snapped shut. Handling the steering wheel in pearl-gray kid gloves, Millard toured the area, showing off. Once he went as far as Cleveland where he found his wife Viola living with a steel worker. She charged him with being a syphilitic and Millard scoffed. She scorned him and Millard boasted, "I'm the boss of Black Lick." When she finally told him imperiously she wanted a divorce, Millard accurately surmised that she was pregnant. "A divorce?" he said. "Nothing I want more."

He did not waste time in reflection about Viola. After all, he was a boss, not realizing it required little courage or quality of mind to be the boss of an economically devastated town where the majority of men did not even have twenty-five cents to play a game of straight pool.

With Leo Basile, the most admiring of his disciples, Millard lost his way. They were driving from Wheeling, West Virginia, to Baltimore after a robbery expedition.

"I know we're not supposed to be on 108," muttered Basile. "I know we're going back toward Pennsy."

"We can't stop now," said Millard, "We've got the rumble seat loaded."

"We could pull off the road when we see a gas station and I could walk over and get a map," offered Leo nervously.

"Okay," said Millard. "Keep your eyes peeled for one and I'll pull over. But *we* won't go in. You will. I don't want to take a chance that some grease monkey will see this stuff and set himself to thinking."

"There's one up ahead," said Leo.

Millard wheeled into a driveway and yanked the emergency brake. "Just go down there and ask them if you can hitchhike a ride to Baltimore on this road. If they tell you no, ask for a map."

Leo left the car and began walking to the gas station. Millard watched him, and then leaned back in his seat, tilted his hat and closed his eyes for a five minute rest. It had been a long, fatiguing day. He and Leo had managed three daylight robberies after driving into Wheeling from Black Lick. In the rumble seat was over one thousand dollars worth of pawnbroker cash. Millard dozed.

Someone ripped open the left door. A flashlight shone. Millard's fluttering eyes could not pierce the glare.

"All right," said a peremptory voice, "you want to get out of there and tell us your business?"

Still blinded, he clambered from the car and confronted a policeman. Another policeman a few yards away was waiting to stop the returning and unsuspecting Leo.

"I just parked here for a minute," protested Millard.

"It's a private driveway," said the policeman. "What do you want with this house? You always park on someone else's property?" By this time the other policeman had gripped Leo's arm. Millard could see the fright on his face.

"And why are you carrying a gun?" asked the first policeman.

As loudly as he could, so Leo could hear, Millard answered, "Douse the light. Look, we're private detectives. It's a confidential case but it's important. Now if this bird here has spotted us, we'd better pull out before he gets wise. You tell us where the station house is and we'll come down there and identify ourselves."

The policeman flicked off his flash. "All right," he said. He gave them the directions and Millard took the pains to fish out his pen and write them down on a small piece of paper, using his wallet as a pad.

"See you in a minute," said the policeman.

Leo opened the door to get into the car.

"Wait a minute," said the other policeman. "Wait a minute. What the hell are two private eyes doing with two silver candelabras in the front seat? What you got in that rumble seat, Mr. Private Detective?"

In time the Maryland police—for Millard and Leo were only twenty-eight miles from Baltimore—traced the stolen goods to West Virginia and transferred the two men to the county jail in Wheeling. Once there, Leo cried incessantly. Millard's assurance that they could do this time standing on their heads did not soothe him.

The press in Blairsville and Black Lick, in heavy type, rejoiced that the robbery ring had been smashed: Wright and Basile were behind bars. It was not news to make Millard's partners comfortable. They worried and, worrying, talked excitedly and indiscriminately. A young police officer, Allen Frye, who wanted to become a detective, listened. Pennsylvania indicted the other three accomplices and lodged detainers and indictments against Millard and Leo.

Millard rarely gave way to fury. But the surprise of these indictments, suddenly served upon him, perfectly detailed and accurate, spelled an additional prison term. He raged.

"Who could have talked?" he shouted to the sobbing Basile. "Who? We had a little stretch to pull in West Virginia, that's all. Now we got a longer one to pull in Pennsy. If someone hadn't talked, the whole thing would have blown over. Who talked? Who?"

He learned soon enough. Basile's sister, Josephine, sent an apologetic letter: "I had to tell Frye," she wrote. "He would have put me in jail if I hadn't. He said the same thing to Salvatore, so

Salvatore had to tell. Frye said Salvatore and I would go to jail, too, for life, and we're your sister and brother."

Allen Frye was a rookie patrolman in Black Lick determined on quick advancement. He had devoted his off hours to implicating Millard in local robberies. Once he threatened the Basiles, the rest was easy.

Millard crushed the letter in his hands. To Basile he said cryptically, "Frye will not get away with this."

Allen Frye didn't. Rookie patrolmen are not expected to solve robberies. Robberies are properly the province of detectives. Rookie patrolmen who do solve robberies earn only enmity from their superiors. Millard wrote Josephine Basile: "After all we did for Frye, this was a fine reward. If this is the way he wants to pay us back, that's the way we'll pay him back. He'll see. Just don't tell anyone."

Josephine did exactly what Millard knew she would: she told everyone. The Blairsville police were also predictable. Three of them visited him in his Wheeling cell.

"What do you know about this Frye? What have you got on him?"

"Frye?" asked Millard. "Who's Frye?"

"Frye's the guy that broke this case. You know who he is."

"Oh, that spoilsport. No, I don't know anything about him."

"You know who he is, though?"

"Yeah, I know who he is. He's the hero of the Blairsville Police Force." Millard smiled. Police officers believe the prisoners who smile at them are smarter and more dangerous than the ones who spit.

Over the next two months, the same officers visited his cell at least once a week. Millard's reluctance beguiled them. They came again and again, fretting while he maintained his composure.

"I wish to God's blue heaven you'd let me alone. You keep bothering me. I've got to face a judge next month and twelve men who are sending me and Basile to a rock pile. And when we get through with that rock pile there's another twelve going to send me and Leo to another rock pile. That's a lot of worry for a man while three detectives keep sitting on the one stool in his cell."

"You ever hear of a concurrent sentence, Wright?"

THE REPEATER | 67

Millard squinted.

"We could put in a word," said the detective, "here and there. You never can tell when you want a word, now and then, here and there."

"Let's say Frye was in on the take," said Millard. "It's my word against his. I'm a con and he's a cop. You know twelve men going to believe me? Why not keep him a patrolman? He'll quit."

Which was what happened. Frye left the force when his superiors jealously charged he had conspired with Millard.

"Call me 'The Manipulator,'" Millard called to Basile when the detectives left.

"Manipulate us out of that four-year stretch," moaned Leo.

"You've been manipulated," Millard shouted.

Revenge, especially that revenge accomplished with cunning instead of brawn, satisfied Millard. Now he had nothing to do but await sentencing.

For their amusement, Millard and Basile had only church. The chapel of the Wheeling jail was in the basement. Its ceiling was laden with intertwining pipes. Rough pews, formed by folding chairs, stretched from the makeshift altar, an old buffet covered with a white sheet. There were no kneeling benches so the prisoners sank to the floor on old rugs.

One Sunday Millard noticed another prisoner across the aisle. A girl. He saw red hair, green eyes, freckles bridging a small nose.

She saw a pale, intelligent face, spectacles rimming dark eyes. He was tall. He was calm. He smiled.

He told her he was in a scrape with the police. He asked if there was any way he could help her when he got his own trouble straightened out, which was just what Genevieve Boyce wanted to hear: Millard was a kind, decent man, fallen afoul of the law. Since she hated the law, she could blame it for Millard's trouble. She told him she was awaiting trial in a Federal court for "helping" her mother; they said she was an accessory before and after the fact.

They fell in love. The guards accommodated their messages. Millard, of course, didn't tell her he had spent almost a quarter of his life in constraint, that his scrape had resulted in two different indictments from West Virginia and Pennsylvania. Not that it would have mattered. Genevieve Boyce was facing conviction for violating the Dwyer Act which made it a federal crime to transport stolen vehicles across state lines. Indeed she had on several occasions, driven stolen cars from Pittsburgh or Charleston to Chicago or Kansas City. Nor did she tell him she had worked as a prostitute since she was fourteen. Nor that she had married one Adam Yates, in order to save him from prosecution as a panderer.

Millard and Genevieve magnified each other's presence so they could make their respective selves anonymous. They lied to each other about that life always out of reach.

Genevieve represented Millard's dream of a life stable and untroubled. Millard was her dream of the breadwinner, the placid man who smoothes out the future and makes the past inconsequential. They dreamed together not so much of things they couldn't have but of things they didn't really want. Millard would always center his love and affection on whores because whores were better prepared to subtract sex from the human equation; Millard disliked the physical proof and exposure of personality— it was a secret he would rather keep for himself.

A life without nervous attenuation, without excitement, without wild distraction would corrode Genevieve Boyce's whole being. She could act and understand only when she conspired and gossiped. She could tolerate prison because conspiracy and gossip filled each day.

Twice they met alone in the cellar chapel. Millard never put his arm around the girl although the guards who had arranged the rendezvous were sure surreptitious sex took place. Millard's chivalry made him more precious to her. Sex to her was a table of contents of villainy and selfishness.

Just before Millard went on trial, Genevieve was sentenced to the Alderston Reformatory for a term not less than two years. Millard and Leo Basile were sentenced to the state penitentiary at Moundsville, West Virginia, there to serve at least two years of a five-year term.

Chapter | 10

Older now, in his mid-twenties, Millard read constantly in prison. His favorite writer was Robert Ingersoll, whom he always referred to as "Bob." Ingersoll had a special meaning for him. Millard considered himself an agnostic, a concept Ingersoll championed; Ingersoll was as well a renowned trial lawyer. Millard was sure he and "Bob" had a lot in common.

His reading, which was voluminous if eclectic, taught him something about the Socratic method. There were, needless to say, these differences between this method and Millard's own: Socrates was intent on truth, Millard on verbal superiority; Socrates wished to win disciples, Millard to provoke the unsophisticated; Socrates sought to know himself, Millard to free himself from his own blame.

As soon as a fellow prisoner took up the thread of an argument, Millard always insisted, "Define your terms." Or he would interrupt with, "I've never heard the word used in that context before. What do you mean?"

To men unused to logical discourse, to men in many respects only a step or two beyond illiteracy, this was a paralyzing experience. They were not so much afraid of losing an argument as they were of betraying before other prisoners that they could not argue at all—with the result that prisoners rarely argued or discoursed with Millard, and his strictures took on some of the authority among convicts that a papal bull has among parish priests.

Millard interpreted his reading romantically; he could not apply it. Millard kept each thinker separated, one from the other, the whole from himself. He isolated each prophet as he was himself isolated in his cell. He never quite appreciated there was an interrelation, say, between Darwin and Marx, or between David Hume and Robert Ingersoll. In short, he never saw the spectrum. Through all the years of his imprisonment Millard went to school and always read, yet he was never educated.

Still, Millard impressed the other prisoners with his erudition. Lawyers save the rich transgressor; and among convicts, a man who asks questions like a lawyer, who talks like a lawyer, is a man eminently capable of his own salvation.

Reading had its way with him. His eyes were bad. Reading worsened them. Millard blamed the physical conditions of prison. He complained his keepers provided poor nutrition, that they weakened his body with tedious and tiring work. A man is what he eats, he insisted. If he had better food, he could read more, improve himself. He weighed only 154 pounds when once he had weighed 170. Prison was breaking down his health. He also blamed prison for robbing him of sexual vitality. The other prisoners boasted of screwing a woman five times a night or bagging three women over the course of a day. Well, if he hadn't been in prison off and on, he told himself, he could have slept with Viola five times a night. He forgot Viola often had to implore him to sleep with her even once. It wasn't his fault. The cooks loaded his food with saltpeter. The commissary sold off the supplies. Prison stripped him of his rights. Convicts, however, have an intense, often inflated, notion of exactly what juridical rights are.

Except for a right to pursue whatever legal remedies are available, to secure review and possible reversal of sentence, a prisoner has no rights. He has no right to bring any action for injury or illness against prison officials regardless of their negligence or carelessness (which explains perhaps the numerous incidence of prison "riots"). Whatever he does in prison, he does by grace of the administrative officials. He has no right to visitors, to letters, to social activities, to food, to cleanliness, to toilet. Prison officials can restrict the books he reads and can limit his library privileges, which in effect can thwart his one available right.

Millard was certainly no better informed than the rest of the prisoners; for that matter, no better informed than the rest of mankind; that the law provided him with certain rights eventually became the demand, voiced silently perhaps, that he was also entitled to certain privileges. When these privileges were not forthcoming, Millard grew bitter.

Bitterness often denies prisoners a chance at the minimal redemptive process. The basis for any society's success is the ability of its people to get along with one another. A successful society needs its criminals to provide a vicarious experience; to break its prohibitions and thus provide a warning of what society can become if everyone releases tensions.

After nineteen months at Moundsville, Millard and Leo Basile were transferred to Ebensburg in Cambria County, Pennsylvania. The Pennsylvania courts sentenced Millard and Leo to another three years. The police, however, had put in the word they promised, and Pennsylvania made the two burglars serve only seven months, counting the sentence in Moundsville as time served.

After his release Millard came home to Black Lick. It was late afternoon when he pushed open the fence gate. On the porch Malcolm Wright sat staring. Millard approached. The father rose from the rocker, walked to the railing, spat, and never said hello.

Millard understood the gesture. He was inured to contempt. He had in these past few years learned how not to integrate disapproval in his experience. Millard did not insist as much as he simply believed that every spell of freedom was a clean slate. He never added up the past and he refused to apologize or feel shame when others did. He marched past his father and unpacked his meager belongings. He had a home; he was safe here; safe as long as he never brought stolen objects to it.

There was a letter from his sister Mabel. She had reclaimed his Ford from the Maryland police; he could have it when he wanted. She had also secured a job for him at the Conemaugh Iron Works in whose office she now worked. And she enclosed a letter to Millard received from Genevieve Boyce. So he had a job, his car, and his sweetheart.

With his first month's pay, Millard filled the tank with gasoline and drove to Steubenville, Ohio, to see Genevieve.

The Steubenville Diner resembled a railroad car. A counter stretched its length. Two griddles, a chopping block, a refrigerator, and a black oven lined the rear wall, a row of stools in front put a man's back to the greasy windows. The walls were slippery with the smoke of fried foods, and the water glasses were forever tarnished with the residue of coagulated soap and the lint of a wet towel. Genevieve, wearing an apron stained with a thousand wipings, stood stock-still in surprise when Millard sidled into a booth, winked, and ordered, "Scrambled eggs, milk, and extra butter on the toast."

He drove Genevieve to her rooming house, promising to stop by before he left the next day.

In the morning, there she was, bag packed, waiting on the curb when Millard parked. All the while Millard laughed with Genevieve on the way back, however, he was thinking, as countless thousands of other young men have thought, "What have I got myself into?"

He had a package on his hands. And he never knew what to do with a package. Millard never heard of giving a girl a buck and the breeze; but then he couldn't distinguish between a lady and a sponger. Millard never had the sense to put on a straw hat and say, "Bye-bye, baby," to a bad habit.

So Millard asked her: "Will you marry me?"

"If you'll sleep with me," she said.

Unknown to him it was a bigamous marriage for her. He never needed a divorce, although he eventually paid a lawyer to obtain one.

Chapter | 11

At the Conemaugh Iron Works, Millard suddenly discovered his years of prison reading had put him into the middle of a union election. He had the vocabulary to describe the attitudes of social reform gaining vogue in the labor movement. His fellow workers nominated him. He ran for the union presidency against an incumbent named McLarn, so ill-prepared and ill-informed about his constituency he never discovered Millard's jail record.

He ran a good race. He lost by sixty votes, which he should have expected since McLarn was the company's man. The election loss disappointed him but then he was a long time learning that the good is not necessarily rewarded because it is the good. The good is rewarded when it's lucky.

Millard didn't want to lose the election, but he may well have wanted to lose Genevieve. He may well have channeled all his energies and attention into union matters to keep himself from her. It had taken him forty-five days after he was married to make love to the pretty baggage.

Genevieve complained. "I'm bored," she said, "and I'm lonely. I'm stuck in this house all day with that deaf man. I want some fun. I want to do something nights."

"I'm busy," Millard insisted. "After I win the election, maybe we'll celebrate."

"I want nicer clothes," she said, pouting. "I want a good time in a pretty dress."

"My father told you to buy anything you needed for the house. What more do you want?" he asked.

She said, "I'm unhappy."

"What right have you got to be unhappy?" Millard asked crossly.

Thus, their relationship deteriorated, and as it deteriorated, it sapped Millard's aspirations for respectability. He took her on an occasional Saturday night to bars and cheap nightclubs with tablecloths soiled by spilled drinks. These expeditions only increased her longings.

"Jesus, I'd like to wake up in a strange room one Sunday morning," she said. She could not abide the bare house, populated by two quiet men who appraised a woman not by her laugh or her body but by the way she fried eggs. At the bars and in the nightclubs, she flirted with strangers, much to Millard's annoyance.

The Saturday night after he had lost the election, Genevieve badgered him about past promises. Millard acquiesced and took her to a garish roadhouse where he winced at the comedian's vulgarities, worried about the price of the weak beer they drank, and lost patience when Genevieve invited two men to their table. He could not contain himself when one of the men jovially patted Genevieve's rear.

"We're getting out of here," he said, all reserve gone.

"What's the matter?" asked one of the men.

"I'm her husband, that's what's the matter."

"He didn't mean anything," protested Genevieve.

"Yeah, I'm sorry. How was I supposed to know it was your wife? I wouldn't bring my wife into a dump like this."

Twisting her wrist, Millard dragged Genevieve out to the car.

"Why did I have to marry a man who lives in the sticks?"

"Because in the sticks you're going to learn how to act like a wife."

"A lot you know about acting like a husband!"

"I earn the living!"

"I could be in Cleveland or Pittsburgh, having a good time

with a couple of fellers, but here I am, in the Pennsylvania cranberry bogs, up to my ass in lost elections."

"You don't like it here," said Millard, tight-lipped and desperate, "pack your bag and get out."

She didn't hesitate. Millard watched her move down the road to the bus stop. When she boarded the early morning Greyhound to Pittsburgh, Millard realized it was no bluff—she was gone.

Her leaving gave him the excuse he had been waiting for. He started burglarizing homes again, telling himself it was she, Genevieve Boyce, who had driven him to it but knowing, too, it was he who let her go, let her go so that the excitement of loss would mount within him, spur him on to risk and chance, make his personality viable again.

Another judge soon enough called him an incorrigible and Millard stepped into another prison, this time the Western State Penitentiary on Pittsburgh's North Side. His behavior was exemplary. The chaplain, whom Millard served as a secretary, persuaded the warden to let Millard organize a school.

The rewards of Millard's faculty were, of course, prestige and special liberties. Millard made his selection from an abundance of applications. Warden and chaplain would have questioned their experiment seriously had they known Millard accepted bribes in return for appointments and that he accepted even bigger bribes in return for diplomas.

Millard was twenty-seven years old when the penitentiary paroled him in November of 1937. On September 28, 1938, two deputy sheriffs deposited him within those walls again, this time to serve a three-to-six-year sentence with another year added for parole violation.

"The school job was here, all the time, waiting for you, Millard," said one of the guards. "It was just as though you never left. We're always happy to welcome back experienced employees."

"I'm glad to be back," said Millard as facetiously. "It will give me a chance to improve the curriculum."

The teaching process always bolstered his concept of himself as a person with intellectual and aesthetic dimensions. Teaching was the power of making over others, transforming them, but during the fourth year of his imprisonment, Millard's eyes began to fail rapidly. He had put them to too extensive a use. The strain gave him headaches and he often suffered through hours of blurred vision, the world looking as though it were under water.

He tried to have other prisoners read to him, but this was expensive and unpredictable. Finally, in 1943, he asked to be relieved of teaching and assigned instead to the prison hospital to give his eyes a rest. He believed his bad vision was a direct result of poor food. The prison hospital furnished convalescents and nursing aides a better diet. Millard was what the other inmates called "cage canny." He knew his way around the interior of the prison. He knew a prison hospital is the best place for the incarcerated burglar to work for there is something there to steal. He stole the meat, usually fresh liver for the patients with pernicious anemia, and sold it to the inmates; he stole drugs, refilling vials with distilled water; he stole surgical instruments. He was never caught. In 1944, when he was again paroled he had over $800 saved from these illicit activities. He had another $200 the prison paid him for his work. That was the sum total this thirty-five-year-old man had accumulated in a life devoted to crime.

Money decides so much of life. Millard knew it.

Chapter | 12

There were jobs for the asking—the war effort had exhausted the labor pool—but they were laboring jobs and Millard thought he deserved something better, that he had a mind and manner which qualified him for a more responsible position. But he couldn't sell himself. Waiting began to deplete his money. He had to take the job the parole officer found him.

He went to work for the Bauer Company which manufactured cement blocks and burial vaults. Cement is hot and it burned holes in the tips of his gloves. His fingers were always blistered. Loading the blocks on a truck was torture. Vault equipment was heavy—wrought-iron gates and marble benches, statuary and monumental vases of stone—and Millard was older now and his muscles were soft.

He lived in a boardinghouse run by two widows, Frieda Wolf, the sixty-eight-year-old mother and her daughter, Ketti Wolf Anderson, a forty-year-old schoolteacher. They didn't knew he was an ex-convict. Millard told them he had spent the last several years in Arizona recuperating from a serious illness. Charmed by his calm, polite demeanor, the two widows fussed over him. They never suspected the telephone calls Millard received every Thursday and Saturday were from the Pennsylvania parole board nor did they think the gentleman who called on Millard every Monday and Friday was a parole officer.

When Millard thought about his fading vision, his poor health, his hopeless employment, a vast weariness washed over him. He could not tighten on the moorings; the world more frequently eluded his grasp as it increasingly eluded his sight. Each day he felt more physically exhausted and dispirited.

Every noon Millard sat in the loading yards, munching a dry sandwich, staring at the surrealistic arrangement of funereal statues.

One day, a pretty girl sat down beside him.

"Who're you?" he asked.

"My name's Roberta. I run the polisher over the finished stones. That's what this apron is for. Mind if I join you?"

"There's stronger men than me you could join," Millard said.

She turned and inspected the ring of Italians and Negroes who, in their undershirts, gambled for pennies every noon, their sweat making their bodies shine.

"That's true," she said. "But I could see you're the only one out here who shouldn't be using his muscles."

They ate lunch together every day after that. Her hair was auburn. She had green eyes and long, graceful hands. When Millard told her one noon he was an ex-convict, he knew the admission wouldn't shock her. There were tight lines about her mouth and there were wrinkles around her eyes; hers was a face from which innocence had long vanished.

Roberta Stuckey was a New Kensington girl. She lived with an aunt who was no better than she had to be. On several occasions Roberta had run away, but she had little to offer an employer save her simple clerical or manual abilities. She worked now as a domestic, now as a waitress. Within her there was a growing need for something better, for an end to her lonely traipsing of tawdry streets.

She was uneducated and many people would confuse her ignorance with stupidity. But she was alert; she would be even more alert if she could catch her breath. Without that pause she knew she could only anticipate a life in which hope became sordid anticipation.

There was no help for her at home, when she was there; only the aging drunken aunt who stole or borrowed or claimed the little money Roberta had. Which may be why she fell in love with Millard Wright when she was nineteen. He didn't ask for her money, he didn't ask for her body. He looked like he would give her something of himself. When she gave him a carefully trimmed sandwich he looked so pleased. He told her she was kind. No one had ever said that before.

That he had been buffeted as badly as she made her compassionate. She decided she'd stay on at Bauer's, even though the pay was low and the work stultifying. She saw Millard every noon hour.

One day, unable to contain herself, she asked, "Do you think something will come of us?"

"We'll see," said Millard.

"When you get straightened out?"

"I hope so," Millard said. And he put his arm around her shoulder.

Something might have come of it, but one morning Millard saw old man Bauer beckon. Bauer said he was firing him. When the shocked Millard asked why, Bauer told him someone had stolen the petty cash box the day before.

"Only you and the nigger were in the office yesterday. I know one of you did it. I don't trust him and I can't trust you because you're a convict. So out you go."

Old man Bauer listened to no appeal.

They had shoved it down his craw again. His throat was constricted with pain. His voice was husky with frustrated rage and self-pity.

Choking, he told Ketti Wolf Anderson, one of his two landladies, that he had lost his job, that he didn't know what he was going to do. He didn't want her to worry; he had some rent money saved.

The middle-aged widow found Millard a courtly man. Nothing attracts a middle-aged widow like a courtly man down on his luck. She came to his bedroom that night and offered herself.

Millard was impotent.

Ketti was bewildered. Everything he said, all his attention led her to believe that he wanted a love affair, that he particularly wanted a love affair with her.

"We can try again," she coaxed. "I don't want you to worry. It's probably my fault."

"It isn't your fault," Millard said huskily. "And it isn't my fault. It's prison. That's why. I've been in prison for most of my life. Prison has done this to me."

That confession was too much for Ketti. She had her standards. Now he had desecrated them. She left, not even bothering to dress, but snatching her clothes from the chair, carrying them balled in her arm, tears coursing down her cheeks.

Ketti did not come from her room the next morning. Frieda, the mother, accosted Millard in the carpeted foyer.

"This man that's coming this morning, that comes every Friday, is a parole officer, isn't he, Millard?" she asked.

"Yes," said Millard, "he's a parole officer."

"I'm not blaming you, Millard. I guess you've paid for what you've done. But I'm going to ask you to leave and Ketti and I want you to leave right away."

"It's Friday," said Millard, pleading. I've got to meet that parole officer who's coming. Could I wait till tomorrow?"

"Right away," Frieda said. "Please don't bother Ketti before you go."

What nagged Millard about women was his realization that a man couldn't put it over on them for long. They appreciated the talk but their covert gauge was virility and their eye was ever on it. They refused to understand a code of honor. It always disappointed Millard to discover chivalry was a means and not an end. He would never turn on them the way they turned on him.

Now he had no home, no money, no job, and no worth. He went to Roberta Stuckey. The drunken aunt took Millard's money before making up the couch. When Roberta crept silently to the couch in the night, and put her hand on his brow, Millard feigned sleep. He could not bear another test. He was gone in the morning. By Monday, the parole officer knew he had disappeared.

For the next two weeks he rifled homes with a frenzy. He neglected all planning. He was a man in a fever. When his car ran out of gas, he boarded a bus laden with radios, jewelry cases, clothes. In growing alarm, the seated passengers pushed toward their windows as Millard, dropping objects in the aisle, made his way toward the back. He had left a mound of suitcases, suits, and kitchen appliances at the bus stop, not noticing them at all as the driver made the bus lurch forward. At the next station, two police cars forced the bus to a stop. With drawn guns, they boarded it and found Millard frantically trying to hide some of his stolen goods under the seats, madly distributing others in the coat racks above.

Millard was tranquil in their custody, ever remote. Literally, one part of him was outside himself. He watched with interest as the policemen unloaded the stolen goods he was transporting. Without their having to tell him, he took his place in the front seat of the police car beside one officer, while the other slipped into the back seat, covering him with a pistol.

Docilely, he entered a cell in the Allegheny County Jail. Apathetically he studied his surroundings. He had never been here before, but like his dream of the familiar street, the cell was utterly known to him. He was experiencing a continuous *déjà vu*. One part of himself kept observing the other. One part couldn't believe he was in jail again, that the other part had committed a series of robberies throughout Mt. Lebanon and Indiana County. One part kept crying to the other that this was the last offense; now the state, as it had warned, would mark him an habitual offender and remand him to jail for life. The true self pitied that other part. And that other self, the criminal self, was too fatigued to care. The fatigue overwhelmed anxiety. With each breath he struggled against laden atmosphere. Each movement became burdensome. Millard's eyes burned.

She came to see him. She was there. Roberta. She sat behind the screen, clutching her little handbag in which she'd carried their sandwiches. Her eyes were bewildered.

"What happened?" she asked when he sat before her.

He could not answer.

She tried again. "I woulda lent you the money."

He bowed his head.

"Aw, fella," she said, "what could have been."

Then she was gone.

He decided to die, to kill himself. Of course! It was the one, the last answer. He was elated over the enterprise. He took a prison spoon and surreptitiously sharpened it by filing it against the rough wall. As soon as he had worn an edge he felt was sharp enough, Millard scraped at the vessels in his feet. He was dismayed when he saw the blood coagulate quickly. He couldn't reach the vein. He began sawing in desperation at his wrists, but the blood flow was meager. He wasn't going to make it. He was too tired to cut anymore. Perspiration poured from him and he began cursing himself. He stamped across his cell back and forth, sobs breaking from him. Finally he made a noose of his belt and wrapping it around the bar at the head of his bed, tried to hang himself by rolling off onto the floor. His unconscious groans and choking awakened the other prisoners. As he fluttered back and forth between consciousness and unconsciousness, gagging and nauseous, he could hear them bellowing for the guards.

Chapter | 13

"There are two ways to understand life: One can live with the poor or one can live with the insane." Millard was sure he remembered some such sentence from one of Robert Ingersoll's books. He was about to test its truth. A lunacy commission had adjudged Millard Wright psychotic, criminally insane. He was remanded to the Farview State Hospital. Millard had found that jail was a place without time. A hospital for the criminally insane —a lunatic asylum—was a place without reason, a place where everything conspired against his getting better. Yet Millard improved. He came back slowly, finding again the ability to put one foot out of the bed after the other, to see that a day spread ahead of him, that there were things in it for him to do, orders he must obey, restraints against which he had to complain.

Eventually, the orderlies removed the straitjacket, moved him from a barren, lonely, steel-doored cell to a room he shared with another man, and then from there to a dormitory, crammed with prisoners, stuffy and close, often dirty, still a place that for the first time in a year gave Millard a glimpse again of society, criminal society, disturbed society, but for all that society, with regulation and movement.

He was on the road to health: he could decipher to what

degree his barracks mates were insane—when they couldn't hear what was requested, when they couldn't add the next minute to the past one, when they forgot they were to participate in an orderly process or couldn't understand the need for that process. He saw other inmates, with only the slightest provocation, fall to the floor in wild fits of masturbation, vicariously transported by hallucinations of a never-interrupted scene of voluptuosity. He saw others from time to time abandon themselves to terrifying fantasies, imagining they were clutched by the paws of a huge rabbit, or that they were deranged children, or that a mysterious reaper had dismembered them. He fought off the sudden violent attacks of sodomites, suffered hearing the constant flow of obscenities, crazed threats, and drooling gibberish.

After a while, the antics only annoyed him, and he was removed. The nurses and attendants no longer spied constantly and incuriously upon him. He was transferred to a corridor with a separate cubicle for himself, able at last to assess his position.

The inmates were thin, emaciated. The food was watery and scarce. That alone was enough to depress him. But he had someone to talk to—the other inmates shut up nightly in neighboring cubicles. They disconcerted him by the information that the Lunacy Commission committed the insane criminal for an indefinite period, any place from fifteen to forty years.

He tried to escape. Most prisoners escape impulsively: a quick dash, a bolt when a guard's attention is diverted; then the wall, the outside; then—where? to the home of a sister or a brother or a mother, to the home of one of those who visit him; sometimes simply to a saloon.

Millard made it to the thickets outside the wire fence where he lay still while guards combed the area. It was cold. Night came on. The escape impulse stopped insisting. Millard rose, teeth chattering, and made his way back to the main gate. In his haste, he had forgotten his glasses.

Now he had convinced his keepers he had to be all the more restrained in the closed ward. Then, not long afterward, one last shock. One of the orderlies approached Millard's bed where he sat day after blank day, the monotony relieved only by a weekly session with a hurried and overworked psychiatrist.

The orderly stood over Millard, snapped his fingers to attract attention and asked, "You with it today, Wright? You hear me?"

"Yes," said Millard, "I hear you."

"It's an important letter. I want to read it to you. You want to listen?"

Millard nodded.

The orderly read him the news that Malcolm Wright had died of a circulatory disorder six days ago. His daughters had buried him in Blairsville.

"You know what that means, Wright?"

"My father is dead. I know what that means. He had an awfully sorry excuse for a son."

The day was no longer empty, it was filled with a yearning for a proper display of grief. In this place? Millard asked himself disgustedly. In here?

He would never find the familiar room at Farview, the recognized corner to call his own, to seek refuge. Living here had taught, as Robert Ingersoll insisted it would, there were worse places than prison. In prison he knew what his jailers expected. The custodians here expected nothing he could fathom, or if they did, they kept it to themselves, burying it past comprehension in the endless sheaf of papers they always rustled. Millard decided in his pain to get back to prison.

The psychiatric staff interviewed him on January 4, 1947. Quietly he answered their questions. Yes, his father's death had affected him; a part of life was now irrecoverable; he could never reward his father's kindness. He thought perhaps it was time he tried to satisfy society's claims against him—they were tough, hard claims, but just claims, a bill he knew he owed. He thought compulsions and conditions beyond his control led him to burglary and then to suicide and escape, but he knew he wasn't as bad as his history made out, that he still hoped to salvage something, if given the chance.

The psychiatric staff recommended to return him to the Allegheny County Jail for trial.

Farview was in Waymart, 360 miles northeast of Pittsburgh. Seated between two guards, Millard felt elation as the car bearing him sped through the desolate countryside. Crusty snow disguised the fenced-in fields. The trees stood as bare spears on the hills. The cows were as stationary as rocks. But this was Outside. Waiting for the stop lights in the small towns, each town nearer Pittsburgh a little larger than the last, Millard watched the passing pedestrians each on a predictable duty. "I am among my own," breathed Millard to himself. Though his hands were manacled and the guards scarcely noticed him, he felt he had secured a lasting freedom. He could endure if his endurance itself was not daily tested by the grotesque.

The car ride filled him with the breath of change.

If only he did not have to go back to prison.

But finally here he was, in the bullpen of the county jail, talking over legal plans with other prisoners, his situation critical because this time he faced a life sentence as an habitual criminal. Still it was better than Farview, just better.

"I'd take the rap in a minute for the Mount Lebanon robberies," Millard told another prisoner. "What is it at the most? Four or five years? I've already pulled some of that at Farview. But if I plead guilty to anything, it means the big count."

"I'll tell you what you already know," said the other. "You need a lawyer. You got the money?"

"I've got several hundred dollars," said Millard. "My sister's holding it."

"That'll get you a lawyer."

"But he's got to be the right lawyer. He's got to plead me not guilty by reason of insanity."

"How can a burglar be insane?" asked his friend. "A jumpy guy can commit a murder. Maybe, he gets nervous, but everyone knows a burglar's a steely one. Every burglar thinks it out."

"The suicide stunt might help me. I need the lawyer who will see it that way."

"The only lawyer I know of who sees it smart for guys like you and me is Lou Little. He just beat a murder rap using that insanity plea. But after all, the guy only shot his wife. You shoulda robbed from relatives. Maybe he could plead you crazy. It's never to anyone's interest to rob from relatives."

Another prisoner told Millard Louis Little was the best, and still another. Prisoners shuffling around a bullpen are supreme experts. And Louis Little was, at this time, the best and probably the most emulated criminal lawyer in Pennsylvania.

Little read the summary Millard had prepared.

"You know some law, don't you?" he asked.

"Yes," said Millard. "I studied."

"Then I don't have to waste time explaining," Little went on. "You know the McNaughton Rule: you must be able to distinguish right from wrong. If you distinguish right from wrong you can be as crazy as a loon and you are still legally responsible for your acts. You managed to tell several policemen, a few psychiatrists, and even more doctors that you knew you were stealing. Mr. Wright, you could commit suicide ten more times and you still wouldn't have a chance in this state for an acquittal. You are a recidivist. Insane or not, I have never known a district attorney or judge to give a recidivist a break. What kind of a chance does that leave you?"

"It may not be much of a chance, but it's the only one."

Little studied the quiet, composed prisoner whose bespectacled eyes earnestly beseeched him.

"Just tell me," Little asked, "what made you steal all this junk anyway?"

Millard shrugged. "Can you take my case?"

"I'll look into it," said Little.

In late February, Little came again.

"Have you come to tell me it's hopeless, Mr. Little?" Millard asked.

"You've talked to the district attorney, haven't you?"

Millard nodded. "He said he wouldn't let me off."

"There might be one way out," said Little. "And I said *might*. There's nothing sure about it. You're a burglar and if you want to take this chance you're going to need the guts of a burglar to go through with it. Because once you do, there's no retracing steps."

"What is it?" asked Millard. "I'll take it."

"A brain operation. Look at this," Little said urgently. "*Life* magazine has an article about this operation which alters personality. It's called a lobotomy." He spread the issue so Millard could read it.

Both of them were quiet while Millard read through the three-page spread.

"But it says they do it to cure sick minds," Millard said. "Why would a doctor do it to me?"

"Read it again," Little ordered. "This operation is supposed to do what prison never did: change you. It says the operation is still in the experimental stage. No doctor has ever lobotomized someone who is well, let alone a criminal. The operation might produce some interesting results, namely that you would give up stealing. Some judge just might want to see if that could happen. If you had the operation he might let you off."

"You think so?"

"We wouldn't submit to it unless we were pretty sure."

"I'd be for it," Millard said, "except it says a patient could lose ten percent of his intelligence. Being a feeble-minded nut would worry me, worry me more than castration. I spent two years in Farview. My intelligence is all I have left." His hand brushed his forehead.

"Never mind forensic gestures," Louis said. "Just think what thirty years in the penitentiary can do to your intelligence. You say you want your self-respect back? Maybe this is the way. Millard, you got yourself stuck on a nail so hard four carpenters can't get you off."

For a moment, Millard was silent. Then he said, "I'm for it. Let me talk to the doctor."

Part Two
THE PENITENT

Chapter | 14

If there was one word which described Lou Little, the word was "oral." He had thick lips which he constantly pursed and constantly fingered. He always talked out of the side of his mouth, slipping words out like fugitives. He was dangerously overweight and food to him was a matter of importance, a matter which he never ceased to discuss. He smoked cigars and clamped his lips around them with the vengeance Chinese bandits once clamped the iron boot on frightened missionaries. He walked as though he were wearing a pair of heavy galoshes, waddling from side to side. He was short, heavy, and a flight of stairs or a long hallway winded him. It was no trouble outdistancing Lou and most men unconsciously did.

There were few men, however, who could outdistance Lou Little before a jury or over a political issue. They never got ahead of him because Lou Little not only knew law but he had a finely honed instinct about which way to jump. He had, also, a positive genius for personal publicity.

By the 1940's, Lou Little was not only a rich man but an important man with important connections. He may have been a gray figure in Pittsburgh and Pennsylvania politics, but he was, for all that, a powerful figure. He wasn't a precinct boss but precinct bosses heard him out.

Though he was a bachelor whose house was filled with cigar and cigarette smoke, littered with discarded shirts and socks, and coffee coppering in day-old paper cups, though his entertaining rarely went beyond the sandwich level, celebrities, Superior Court judges, lawyers, politicians, and others were always quick to accept Lou's invitation. Lou was a man who could make a deal, and everyone who cannot make a deal needs a deal from time to time. When people need a deal, they will importune the man who can make one. Because he could manage a deal hundreds of people stayed pals with him. One of these was Yale David Koskoff, a neurosurgeon, then the Research Director of Montefiore Hospital's Neurological Department.

Sometime before, Koskoff had gone to Little to ask his help in the dismaying delay he and his wife faced in an adoption proceeding. Koskoff hoped Little could at most initiate a suit to speed up the process. But Little owned political leverage and he brought it to bear, exchanging one favor for another perhaps, and what the Koskoffs thought was a matter of years to adjudicate was no more than a matter of weeks.

So when Little called him about Millard, Koskoff naturally said they would talk, although his first reaction was amazement that Lou would suggest a lobotomy for a criminal, amazement because the prospect was outrageous. By the time Lou Little came to see Koskoff two days later, Koskoff was turning over the prospect in his mind, wanting to do it, needing one more compelling reason to go ahead.

"This Millard Wright isn't really a hoodlum," Lou Little said. "As a matter of fact, if you didn't see him in jail, you'd think he taught high school. He's soft-spoken, polite, smart."

"Why do you need something as radical as a frontal lobotomy to salvage him?" Koskoff asked. "He must have had therapy at Farview. What about setting up an extensive program for continuing it?"

"Not a chance, David. There are three types of crime a professional never gives up. One is prostitution, a second is forgery, and a third is burglary. Once they learn, they cannot stay away. It's too easy. Every judge knows prostitution, forgery, and burglary have the highest incidence of recidivism—repeaters, in layman's language."

"Maybe the profits have hardened this Wright?" Koskoff pursued.

"No, not profit," Little replied. "He's compelled. You told me once a lobotomy can relieve compulsions."

Koskoff wanted to perform this lobotomy for several reasons. He wanted to do it because he was familiar with and expert in the technique; because he believed in it, and because Millard Wright needed help. They were all good reasons. But the real reason, the reason Koskoff knew he would operate on Millard was that this was that once in a lifetime chance: this was the undamaged man, the cells of the brain not deteriorated, the mind not deluded. A lobotomy here could lead to a better understanding of the frontal lobe function. This man could become the experimental control with whom to compare the results obtained in lobotomizing sick men, for criminality per se is not an illness.

"Have you thought of any other doctor?" asked Koskoff, breaking his silence.

"No," said Little, "I was pretty sure you'd do it."

"I want to do it," said Koskoff. "The question is how and when."

"The courts may not indulge us, in which case you won't be able to do it," Little said. "But if I find a judge and a district attorney who say it's worth a chance, I can count on you, right?"

"It's risky," Koskoff said. "All operations are risky. This one is riskier than most. Not only risky for Millard Wright but risky for you and me."

"Millard Wright has taken more than his share of risks. It's in the cards one of them ought to pay off."

"Yes," Koskoff answered, "if the courts and the prosecutor and this Millard say 'operate,' I will do it."

"There are risks we take because they're worth it," Lou said, reaching forward to shake his hand.

"I'd like to know one thing, Lou. Why? I'm ready to take the risks but I want to know why you want to take them? Why you want Millard Wright and me to take them?"

Lou wrapped his mouth around the cigar and puffed heavily before he answered: "Maybe I want to participate in a pioneering medical adventure, but you don't believe that. Maybe I want my picture in the paper—national publicity—you might believe that.

Maybe I just thought this was a good idea. How about that? That's the why. Will you accept that?" Now he pointed the cigar at Koskoff and said, "You're questioning my motives, Doctor, and if you questioned every lawyer's motives, no one would ever win acquittal."

Chapter | 15

The March day was unusually bright for Pittsburgh. A light breeze blew the smog to the hill crests. A warm sun promised a green spring. At noon, Koskoff walked from his office to the William Penn Hotel to meet Judge A. Marshall Thompson and Lou Little.

Koskoff passed through the lobby to the main dining room, where he saw both Thompson and Little on the far side, sitting at a round table. The sun streamed through large glass windows which descended from the ceiling to the floor. The heavy damask curtains had been pulled back to admit more light. The dining room was filling up and the china rattled on the trays as waiters bustled back and forth.

Energy, effort, change: these three men felt all. Lou, looking like an overfed juvenile, sat gesticulating at the side of the Judge, whose white hair seized the sunlight. Until the moment Koskoff stepped into this tableau, the lobotomy was still an unrealized, perhaps unrealizable, prospect. Once they accomplished their introductions, Koskoff knew it would happen.

Significantly, Thompson's first words were, "We may all play roles in this situation. What will yours be, Doctor?"

The table was covered with a heavy linen cloth on top of

which was set an elaborate service. Before the hour passed, Koskoff had moved his service aside to sketch the imaginary outlines of the human brain. The Judge, whose dignity was impeccable, even shifted his chair at one point for a better view of these contours. Lou kept straddling the table, emitting only a low whistle when Koskoff made a quick X where the incisions would go.

"How many patients have you lobotomized?" the Judge asked.

"I've lobotomized about fifty patients at Western Psychiatric Hospital, most of them psychotics. One third recovered, one third improved, one third showed no change."

"But Millard Wright isn't psychotic, is he?" Judge Thompson asked. He had an immense judicial presence. His questions commanded succinct logical answers, yes or no answers.

"No, but he is suffering," Koskoff answered. "Perhaps that is why I am willing to help. If he consents to this operation, I want this opportunity to study a man intensively before and after a lobotomy. The fact that Wright is healthy makes him important to me and to neurology because illness introduces its own behavioral characteristics. I don't think there is any question he is afflicted but not physically, psychologically."

"That's a pretty good definition of a recidivist," the Judge said. "You don't think he's a criminal by nature?"

"He hasn't been proved guilty yet," interrupted Lou Little, who had a genius for knowing the precise moment to interrupt.

With a nod, the Judge turned and asked, "Now tell me your role, Mr. Little."

"If we can go ahead with the experiment, and you preside over his trial, I'm going to advise Millard to waive a jury. If you don't preside, I'll try to convince twelve men that the lobotomy is sufficient expiation for the past and that an immediate parole is not an excessive reward."

"You're after a deal," Judge Thompson said flatly, smiling.

"Absolutely," Lou said. "No one doubts Wright pulled those robberies in Mount Lebanon—not me, not Bill O'Donnell, the assistant district attorney, not you. But Bill said he might go along with this lobotomy, at least go along by not insisting on imprisonment. That leaves it up to the Court and to Wright. Now, your Honor, what do you say?"

Thompson stared for a moment at the gilded ceiling before fixing his gray eyes first on Lou, then on Koskoff. "I say neither yes nor no. The dining room of the William Penn Hotel is no place for the Court to arrive at a decision. But I can advise you if Wright brings the Court a petition, I will consider it."

"I think you can count on Wright's doing that," Lou said.

"Then I had better explain my role," Thompson said. "I sit on the bench to see that the law keeps its promises. The law made a promise to protect both of you from predators and it promised Millard Wright to punish predatory actions. Now the law can put aside these promises if it has a good reason. That's what you gentlemen want to offer, isn't it? Good reasons?"

Lou rubbed his hands and asked, "Then we can go ahead? I want Wright to undergo a psychiatric examination and I want Koskoff to start his work.

Koskoff did not say, "What about that 'if'? What if this is not a good reason?" He could have said it, the thought crossed his mind, but he wanted to get on with it too.

"You can go ahead," said the Judge.

The next day he issued a writ:

It is ordered and decreed that Dr. D. I. Jamison and Yale David Koskoff, physicians, be permitted to examine the said Millard Filmore Wright in the County Jail of Allegheny County Pennsylvania between the hours of 9 A.M. and 9 P.M. and that Louis Little, Atty for defendant, and Wm. O'Donnell, Ass't District Atty, may be present.

Chapter | 16

Millard was without his eyeglasses. They were in his hands and he was wiping them carefully over and over with a clean folded handkerchief. It was a rare occurrence for anyone to see Millard without his thick lenses, though the visitors he awaited did not know this. The studied swipes, the inspection, and re-inspection were self-conscious gestures.

He waited at the corner of a rectangular table in the visitors' room, behind a large half-moon window with ascending and descending prison bars. Two guards had rolled away the wired-glass barrier. He was dressed in a gray shirt with a number stenciled over his pocket. He wore black pants without a belt. He had neither pencil nor pad nor cigarettes. Yet, though at a disadvantage, he was the most aggressive man in the room when his visitors arrived.

They were Lou Little, Assistant District Attorney William O'Donnell, Dr. Daniel Jamison, a psychiatrist versed in forensic medicine, and Yale Koskoff, whom Little had described as the best neurosurgeon in the city.

Koskoff was almost as tall as Millard but he had broader shoulders and his gestures revealed a greater physical tension. He was dark, his eyes gray, and he smiled often. The others who filed into the room looked at Millard as they would look at a curiosity.

But Koskoff, long a specialist, knew exactly how to treat a patient. Already he was exercising the proprietary attitudes of the specialist toward a confused, bewildered sick man.

Millard, who had never played poker, nor completed an advantageous business deal, nor discussed his curriculum with a graduate-school dean, still intuited immediately that as a patient he would ease himself in as an equal. He was the patient afflicted with a unique disease, one so rare he would not have to importune the doctors for health, rather they would importune him to let them find the cure.

Millard could see that William O'Donnell was anything but the hardened state's attorney. He was a gentle, gracious man, often semidetached because of the pity welling within him for defendants. He had humor, imagination, and a theatrical turn of mind which should have made his practice rival that of Lou Little's; but over and over, O'Donnell had succumbed to alcohol and before he would destroy his health and his mind, he went into the district attorney's office where the pressures were less and so were the rewards. Millard, who knew, would never mistake him for a cop.

Jamison was the oldest of the three men, conservative in dress and manner, personally quiet, but acute. Millard guessed right away, Jamison's permission was as necessary as Koskoff's volunteering. If both agreed, O'Donnell was sure to go along. Millard put on his glasses and squinted until his eyes focused. He rose to shake hands with the four men. Then he let Lou Little do the talking.

When Little finished, Millard turned expectantly to Koskoff. The doctor started to explain. Millard already knew much of the theory. Now it was his turn, his turn to play the provocative student, the student who knows the answers and astounds the professor with his questions.

"What technique do you use, Dr. Koskoff?"

"The one you saw in *Life* magazine. I learned this technique from Dr. Poppen at Boston Psychiatric Hospital."

"What about trephination? Large or small?"

"The discs will be large. Their removal will let me perform the operation under direct vision."

"Which areas of my frontal lobes do you have to cut?" Millard asked.

"I think it is a matter of how much I cut rather than where."

"Isn't the purpose to separate the id from the ego and super-ego?" The pupil was taking over the lesson.

"Id, ego, and superego aren't in any specific locale," Koskoff said. "You're thinking of an artist's conception, a two-dimensional conception. Mind has many more dimensions, more than three, probably manifold dimensions. Yet in a small way, Mr. Wright, you're not wholly wrong. A lobotomy will affect id, ego, and superego."

Behind them Dan Jamison stirred restlessly. The criminal was conversant with Freudian terminology. But he was an amateur and like most amateurs he failed to realize psychiatric terms are often linguistic conveniences.

"Millard," Koskoff asked, "ever read Shakespeare? Ever read Henry the Fourth, Part Two?"

"Yes," he said.

"Then imagine the ego as Prince Hal legislating between Hotspur, the superego because he's proud, and Falstaff, the id because he's sensual and irresponsible. Remember what happens at the end?"

"Prince Hal defeats Hotspur."

"And he says to Falstaff, 'I know thee not, old man.' That's a metaphoric picture of the healthy mind. I've borrowed it from Freud. Your Prince Hal can't vanquish the Hotspur who wants to steal for gratification nor can it discourage the Falstaff who wants punishment."

Millard never liked the play taken away from him. He disliked a dialogue which dismissed his arguments.

"That's not very scientific," he said. "What kind of a guarantee is that?"

"Science makes no guarantees," Koskoff said patiently. "A guarantee is the last thing any of us can offer in this situation."

"Why would you want to operate on me?" he asked. There was the barest hostility in the question. Before Koskoff could bring himself to say, "*Your* lawyer made the request," Millard went on, "I'm a guinea pig, right?"

"Not a guinea pig," Lou Little interrupted, "you're a man

courageous enough to suffer the hazards of a brain operation to help science."

Rhetoric, Koskoff thought.

But Millard grasped the point and turning to O'Donnell said, "The idea would be that I go free to test the operation." He poised for the answer.

"Only the court can decide that," O'Donnell said. "No one is forcing you into a lobotomy."

Millard shrugged.

"I wouldn't lobotomize a perfectly normal man who is going to spend the rest of his life in jail," Koskoff said.

"And no court will let you," said Lou Little.

These were honest men. Millard heard them pledging his security. This was a promise. "Do you think this operation will stop me from stealing?" he asked.

"That's what we're going to test," answered Koskoff.

"What will it do definitely?"

"It will probably stop you from dreaming and it will reduce your creative powers."

"How about my chess game?"

"Lobotomy would affect a Reshevsky or a Capablanca, but you should still play with your usual facility. By creative powers I mean it would be harder to write music after a lobotomy than it would be to practice medicine."

"How about memory?"

"It will make you more tranquil and, hopefully, more effective. New memories may replace old."

Millard sensed at this moment that they had stopped feeling sorry for him. He wanted persuasion and praise and they were becoming matter-of-fact. "New memories?" he asked.

"A lobotomy may influence memory processes so that new associations may be more effective than old ones."

"More effective?" Millard snorted. "Why don't you recommend lobotomy for everyone?"

Koskoff's eyes twinkled. The other men were laughing.

Millard said to Koskoff, "If you're game, I am."

Koskoff shook hands over the prospect. As of now, they were in it together.

Chapter | 17

What excited Millard as he left the room, the omnipresent guard beside him, was that these men wanted to do this more than he did. It excited him that it was he who had finally put the act in motion; it was he who would fulfill it. That is what they wanted—fulfillment.

There was something else he had established that was important to him: he was not a man, defenseless though he might be, that they could figure out.

The guard and he exchanged indifferent glances as they waited for the elevator. "What's that all about in there?" asked the guard, "with the D.A. and the alienist and the others? What have you got to stool about? You got something on the Communists?"

"The Communists are going to know all about me. I'm going into history books."

"Hah!" snorted the guard.

"We'll see," said Millard. With perfect superiority he stepped ahead of his keeper into the elevator.

He had said yes. When he met these men this afternoon he had been trepidatious. Now that trepidation had given way to elation. Why had he been so cautious, so worried? Koskoff knew what he was doing. Lou Little told him Koskoff was famous. Here was that famous man needing him, Millard Wright, needing Millard Wright's mind where the state was only annoyed at having to pen up his body.

Finally he had done something. Finally he had done something which took all his courage and his intelligence to decide to do. He was sure it would be worth it. He was going to become another man, a different man, born again. The lobotomy would slice that band of misery which squeezed, always squeezed his hopes.

They passed from the elevator into the bullpen, a gigantic rectangle which spawned cell after cell populated by stunned and listless men, marking time as best they could by murmured argument, fervent advice, illusory hope. The place was sour. The smell of vomit from the snoring drunks permeated Millard's cell. One of the toilet bowls in another area had jammed and the stench of excrement assailed the place. Everyone contended, too, with the smell of sweaty wool. Until they were arraigned, the prisoners had no chance to shower.

Millard stepped into his cell and turned and said to the guard, "I'm getting out of here. You know why? Because I'm going to do something for somebody, for society."

"Do something for me," said the guard, sliding the barred door shut. "Cut them gab-fests short. I'm a half hour into the next shift."

One of the prisoners, leaning idly against the bars, studied Millard and said, "You know, con, you look happier than if you'd been sprung."

"Funny thing," said Millard. "I am happier than if I'd been sprung."

It was true. Millard did not have to articulate it to himself to know it was true. He loved hospitals, even prison hospitals. The antiseptic odor guaranteed cleanliness. In a hospital there was pity, concern, and comfort. It was the one place a man could relax. The sicker a man was, the more a hospital revolved around him. And this time, though the hospital revolved around him, he was going to be healthy, he was going to be new.

"This time when I get sprung," he said to the anonymous

cellmate, "this time I have more than a chance at the other end."

For there it was—applause, spontaneous praise, admiration, that social approval which would tell him at last what he was and, once defined, find at last true direction.

"When do we get started?" he asked Lou Little the next day.

"Right now," said Little, clamping on his cigar as he opened his briefcase. "This is your petition. Sign it. Then we file it with the Court."

Millard signed.

"You don't want to read it?" asked Little.

"I trust you," said Millard. "You and Dr. Koskoff know that."

Little stuffed the petition into his briefcase, buckled it and said, "It should take a week or two. That's all."

It was that easy for this burglar to make a judgment permitting himself to be turned from a human being into an experimental object. The proposal was bizarre, the experiment might degrade him, but he was sure it would not. He was confident that, instead, it would elevate him, help him find the rhythm of a useful, important life.

Lou Little filed the petition in which "Petitioner agreed voluntarily and without any promise or duress that it would be to his benefit and for the benefit of society that he submit himself to an operation on his brain known as a frontal lobotomy. Petitioner believes he is in need of such an operation as aforementioned to make him a useful member of society and to remove or attempt to remove from him the criminal tendencies with which he has been addicted since his boyhood and from the uncontrollable urge and desire to commit burglaries and such other crimes known to the law as felonies."

On the eighteenth of March, the Court granted the petition. Judge Thompson ordered that Millard Wright be removed to the Montefiore Hospital to undergo a frontal lobotomy and afterward returned to the Allegheny County Jail to await trial.

Chapter | 18

In 1913, Hideyo Noguchi, a Japanese physician who worked at the Rockefeller Institute, discovered that a psychiatric disorder, general paresis, was caused by the syphilis organism. Not too long before, Koch and Pasteur had established that a specific organism caused a specific disease. A doctor no longer had to administer to a universe, he had to treat an organism. Disease was not infinite; like our universe, it was finite, it had limits.

A universe has frontier after frontier, however, and medicine's next frontier lay in the knowledge that disease is also the result of chemical and psychological imbalances. A man with an ax in his hand, about to bludgeon an·innocent, is no healthier than a man shaking with Parkinson's Disease, unable to hold a pencil. There are therapies and cures. Medicine is sure of it. But it often takes a lifetime and sometimes several generations to discover or invent them.

Until he met Millard Wright, David Koskoff was mainly concerned with the business of healing. David Koskoff was a brilliant mechanic. As doctors put it, Koskoff could "cut" with the best of them. Certainly he was a doctor other doctors admired. His surgical judgment was sound. He knew how to cut quickly, cleanly, and precisely, how to instruct a nurse as to what a surgeon needed, how to teach an intern what he had to do.

As an intern in Boston City Hospital before antibiotics were developed, Koskoff had treated many a child stricken with meningococcic meningitis for whom the disease was fatal. He remembered these futile efforts whenever he tried to explain to an intern who never expected to see a case of meningitis, let alone treat one, by what symptoms a doctor could recognize the disease. At moments like these, Koskoff realized that in the course of his own lifetime medicine had conquered the microbic and epidemic diseases. It was time to move on.

John Fulton, of the Neurophysiology Laboratory at Yale, who had devised the experimental lobotomy for the apes Becky and Lucy, taught Koskoff that a harmony between mind, body, and environment could be restored by a physical lessening of anxiety, while his readings of Freud, whose singular contribution was the discovery that everything is motivated, taught him that harmony could be restored by calming the built-in resources of self-destruction and neglect. That harmony was the only way Koskoff could define health just as the only way he could define disease was to guess along with others that it was an inability to withstand ordinary interruptions within the environment.

In 1936, at the age of thirty, Koskoff came to Pittsburgh as the Staff Head of the Department of Neurosurgery at Montefiore Hospital. Before that he had worked in Baptist Hospital in Boston and then the Lahey Clinic. Koskoff arrived in Pittsburgh as a friendless stranger, wondering if anyone would ever know his name. Less than twelve years later, he was as well-known a neurosurgeon as Lou Little was a lawyer.

But as soon as Millard Wright said he would undergo the lobotomy, David Koskoff began to learn what losing favor can mean. When things begin to go against a man, he needs determination, and God help him sometimes for his determination.

Koskoff wanted to perform the operation at Western State Psychiatric Hospital, a new complex recently completed by the Commonwealth for teaching and research. Its facilities were excellent. More, Koskoff wanted the staff psychiatrists and psychologists to aid him in the intensive personality study he proposed to make of Millard.

He approached Dr. Grovesnor Pearson, Western State's first

director, who had appointed Koskoff as Consultant in Neurosurgery. He told him about the lobotomy. Koskoff was sure Pearson would welcome the chance to have his hospital and staff collaborate in what might be a significant and pioneering investigation.

Pearson was adamant. He said no. He said he wouldn't argue the matter, and he was as good as his word.

Standing in the hall after their meeting, Koskoff felt uneasy. Dr. Pearson had asserted his authority, asserted it at his expense. A colleague had given him a no when he fully expected an enthusiastic yes. A friend had said he wouldn't take chances with Koskoff.

Supposing he couldn't find a hospital?

Sidney Bergman, the new Executive Director of Montefiore Hospital, was thoroughly familiar with the work of Sheldon and Eleanor Glueck of Boston, who had undertaken extensive research in the fields of criminology, psychiatry, and the law. Millard Wright interested him. Bergman had a wide humanistic streak. He had been graduated from the Boston Latin School and Harvard University. While he was aware that experimentation involved risks, he was aware that calculated risks tested positively more often than not.

Sidney Bergman liked to talk and ideas excited him. Once Koskoff broached the idea, explained that he needed the facilities of Montefiore to perform a frontal lobotomy on a criminal, Bergman was on his feet, walking around his desk, pounding the neat glass surface, as he told himself and Koskoff what success in such a venture could mean.

"Sidney," Koskoff demurred, "the project, if I can refer to Millard as a project, is not going to meet with unqualified approval."

"Approval doesn't interest me," Sidney said. "All of us spend too much time looking for love and approval. Montefiore is a general hospital. We're here for the citizens of Pittsburgh, from the kid who breaks his leg playing football to the corporation president who doesn't know what the pain in his belly is."

"Millard Wright isn't as innocent as a kid with a broken leg or as substantial as a corporation president."

"Montefiore has room for all of them," said Bergman. "You go ahead. Count on all our cooperation and help."

Chapter | 19

Just before noon on March 21, 1947, a guard unceremoniously beckoned to Millard.

"You being transferred?" he asked. "To Montefiore Hospital?"

"I think so," Millard said, "but I haven't seen my lawyer about it."

"I don't know anything about your lawyer," the guard said. "I got a court order here to transfer you."

At the check-out desk, Millard claimed his meager belongings, including a wallet with all the money he had, and signed the perfunctory receipt. The guard turned him over to two deputies from the sheriff's office who just as unceremoniously drove him across the city.

He expected to see Koskoff or Little at the hospital but he met only an efficient girl at the Admissions Office. She gave Millard a cursory glance when one of the deputies asked, "You prepared to admit Wright?"

All she asked was, "You're Doctor Koskoff's patient?"

Millard nodded yes and she began to assemble a sheaf of forms on her desk, interrupting her work every now and then to point where she wanted Millard's signature. She didn't even ask him the reasons for his admittance. She quickly typed a name tag, strapped it around his wrist and told the deputies brusquely where the room was.

A nurse appeared, gestured Millard to the bed, took his temperature, blood pressure, asked him a series of questions about his general health and when he tried to elaborate, said curtly, "Please. Just yes or no."

The hospital universe was not revolving around him after all. He had become part of the process, a process which exists for its own ends, not for the factors fed into it. Millard was just another integer and not a particularly sick integer at that.

But it was still his mind on which the process would experiment. "Every time I lend myself," he said, "I play the patsy." He had admired Crook Forsha and Crook Forsha let him take the rap for the theft of two tires. He trusted a lawyer to make his bail and the lawyer absconded with the money. Benny wanted to use him. Viola married him to indulge devious promiscuity. Now Lou Little and Dr. Koskoff. Why weren't they here? This was his supreme effort and he wanted reassurance for that effort, respectable voices telling him yes, this was the right thing to do. This would make him a hero. This would make him remembered.

"Where are you going?" asked the deputy posted outside his door.

"To get a pen and paper," Millard said. "I want to write a letter."

"You got a little button in the room. Press it."

"I gotta write the doctor," Millard said. "It's important."

"That room's a cell and I'm your keeper. Press the buzzer."

He did not know what to say to Dr. Koskoff when he finally got his writing materials. So he asked for favors. He wanted a complete physical. He wanted an ophthalmologist. He wrote, "My present eye ailment has contributed largely to my return to crime. I have great confidence in you. Your personality, your genuine interest, your obvious faith in yourself were the factors that brought about my decision. May we advance surgery together."

Millard was shrewd enough to guess the letter would disconcert Koskoff. It made him sad to realize there was no one else he could disconcert, no friends, his sisters scattered, no idea where Roberta Stuckey was.

His letter did disconcert Koskoff, but not in the way Millard intended. Koskoff was used to patients and the families of patients instructing him. The letter disconcerted him because Millard was overly concerned with body problems. The locus of the man's despair was not in his body; it was in his mind and in his surroundings. And Koskoff had made every arrangement he thought Millard needed. He had scheduled a physical, an eye examination, a group of psychologists to administer tests.

The next day both doctor and patient were disconcerted beyond all patience.

SCALPEL VERSUS CELLBLOCK read the headline in the Pittsburgh *Post-Gazette.* "BRAIN SURGERY MAY GIVE CRIMINAL NEW LIFE." No one imagines the power of that young man in the back of the courtroom, slouched in his seat, hat on his knee, distant and detached except for his occasional jokes with the bailiffs, that young man so often inattentive to the proceedings. He is the courtroom reporter. It may be pedantic to complain that in this instance neither the reporter nor his editor had any idea of precisely what a frontal lobotomy was. Which meant the public didn't know. All the public thought it knew was that a criminal was being given kid-glove treatment.

The following morning, the Associated Press put the story on the wire and the *New York Times,* along with scores of other papers, headlined: FELON TO HAVE OPERATION ON BRAIN TO END CRIMES.

That evening, there was a follow-up story in the *Post-Gazette:*

Millard Wright walks down a shady street at night and something shouts within him "steal, steal, steal," and with all the cunning of an intelligent man, he enters a house and pillages it. Can a brain operation, called by surgeons a "frontal lobotomy," severing his primitive impulse to steal from his intellect, make Millard Wright a man who fears no shady street? Wright, 36, is willing to take the chance. The neuro-surgeon who will perform the short but delicate surgery is Dr. Yale David Koskoff. The big question is whether it will make Millard Wright a good citizen. One prominent psychiatrist said it was "highly possible" that if Wright was the victim of a "compulsion to steal" that the operation would carry out its purpose. Millard Wright, who calls Black Lick his home when he is not incarcerated, is no ordinary house burglar. A Behavior Clinic examination showed that he was above average intelligence and his knowledge is such that when in the Western Penitentiary he taught English to other prisoners. A letter to his attorney, Louis Little, made references to Dostoievsky, the Russian writer, and to Thomas Paine, Huxley, Spencer and even Goethe. He's tall, and thin, and professional looking. Assistant District Attorney William O'Donnell described him as being extremely rational and lacking in braggadocio. All who have talked to him have agreed that if Wright was to knowingly go on a life of crime, that his smooth manner, his large vocabulary, would make him an ideal "confidence man." Time will tell the ending of the undertaking. Only then, when Millard Wright, tall and thin, walks down a shady street, and something says, "steal, steal, steal," but something shouts louder, "don't do it." . . . time will tell.

To compound this sensationalism, on that Sunday, a magazine supplement ran a cover story about Millard which informed readers Koskoff was about to "cut evil from a man's brain."

Publicity is merciless. Publicity disturbs the equilibrium of life much as a low-pressure area disturbs the equilibrium of the weather. It creates a partial vacuum. And into that vacuum rush contending elements.

Millard, waiting idly in his room, read these stories, first with interest, then with mounting regret. He reacted to the stories as all men react: some of the facts were wrong. These facts happened to constitute him and there was no reason they should be wrong instead of right.

Yet he thought the facts made him important. The more he thought about it, the more he realized they only made him *seem* important. No voices ever shouted in his ear "steal, steal, steal," and the psychiatrist talked about him as dispassionately as he would talk about a butterfly on a pin. Millard knew exactly what the reporters were doing: They were remaking him into a freak.

Koskoff read the news stories and they worried him, too. He consulted with Lou Little.

"There's nothing you can do about it," Lou Little told him. "Nothing. Wait it out. They're not going to write about it forever."

"The weekly magazines have already called my office."

"Just momentary publicity," he said.

Patiently Koskoff explained. "Lou, every time a reporter says 'The eminent Dr. Koskoff' the Allegheny County Medical Society reads 'notorious.'"

"David, this is a news story. I'll tell you what I tell my clients and what I've told Millard: say nothing. Saying nothing won't stop reporters digging around anymore than not making an echo will stop an avalanche. But it's the best we can manage under the circumstances."

"But I cannot have it!" Koskoff exclaimed.

"I never knew a newsman wouldn't turn in his grandmother for a headline. If there had been a reporter who understood it, he would have stolen Einstein's theory of relativity and then had his editor insist it was freedom of the press. You undertook this experiment, David, and you can't presume you're a private person. Because if it works, you're going to want to be a public person, damn right you are."

Dr. Edward Mayer, chief of the Allegheny County Behavior Clinic, told a reporter "the chances of Millard Wright realizing his hopes of becoming a respectable member of society appear vague." That statement prompted Sidney Bergman, who had offered Montefiore's facilities, to pay Koskoff a visit.

Bergman hadn't come to renege, but he told Koskoff several of Montefiore's trustees had complained. One of the trustees had even called Koskoff a quack. The publicity was unpleasant. When Koskoff confessed there was little he could do about it, Bergman asked if he couldn't operate immediately, within the week? Koskoff explained he had accepted Millard as a patient in order to make an intensive study of a normal neural system before lobotomy. He couldn't let the press force his hand any more than he could let a patient's family dictate his moves. The earliest he could operate was mid-April.

"You may wish by then," sighed Bergman, "you had operated tomorrow or the next day."

Koskoff visited Millard on the evening of his second day in Montefiore. He was still in his prison uniform. The hospital hadn't yet issued him pajamas, robe, or slippers, nor had he shaved. He was depressed and excessively casual.

Sitting on the edge of the bed, swinging his bare feet, he didn't rise when Koskoff came in but said, almost sullenly, "You've come to tell me it's all off, haven't you?"

"What makes you think it's off?" Koskoff asked.

"The publicity. No one's told me a thing."

"I was waiting for your medical report."

"What does it say?"

"Kerataconus. Your eyes. You know that."

"Is that why you're calling it off?" His voice was plaintive. But he was manipulating.

"No," Koskoff said, "I'm not calling it off. You may want to call it off. Do you? Tell me."

"There isn't a chance I can call it off." He buried his head in his hands.

Koskoff waited.

Millard threw one of the papers from his bed to the floor and said, finally facing the doctor, "Did you read that? What they said? That I'm an arch-criminal? A crooked mastermind. Before all this broke, I might have pulled a twenty-to-life sentence. You know what I'll get now? I'll get life plus ninety-nine."

"I think you're exaggerating."

"*This* I know, Doctor. Get your name on the front page for any rap and you go forever. I can't pull out. And if you pull out, I can bet now not one other doctor is going to think twice about me. No one will do this lobotomy if it isn't you."

"If it weren't for the publicity, Millard, would you want to cancel the experiment?"

"It may look like I do," he said, "but I don't. I want you to help me."

"I'll see that you have some hospital clothing," Koskoff said. "Maybe it would be better for both of us if we didn't read the newspapers. You promised to write me an autobiography and you have a great many psychological tests to take between now and then."

They had to enjoy an immense conceit, Millard to go through with it, Koskoff to persevere. They had every reason to call it off at this moment: Millard because the papers frightened him, Koskoff because the papers threatened him. A conceited man who pledges a friendship will always insist on proving that friendship, sometimes to his own disadvantage, sometimes to his friend's.

When Koskoff returned home that night, he was fatigued by the problem of Millard Wright and hospitals and court orders but not so fatigued that he didn't open a letter from the Executive Secretary of the Allegheny County Medical Society. By registered mail, the Executive Secretary told him a complaint had been lodged against his behavior, alleging he had violated the Society's rules by encouraging unethical publicity.

He hurled the letter into the wastebasket. It had informed him he was to appear in his own defense before the Judicial Committee on April 14, 1947, at 4 P.M.

If they censured him, he would have no choice but to call off the operation. If he operated in defiance of such a ruling, the Society would suspend his membership. Without membership, his position in any Pittsburgh hospital was precarious. Without hospital facilities, there was no way he could perform brain surgery.

There it was. Trouble.

For the first time, he thought of the lobotomy as a fruitless, unpromising, sterile, painful prospect. Had he not paid this visit to Millard Wright tonight, he would have called it off. There had been many occasions when he decided for one reason or another not to subject a patient to a brain operation already scheduled. Always, he made these decisions for a patient's betterment or comfort. But this wasn't true of Millard. He, Lou Little, and Judge Thompson had compromised Millard, though Millard had willingly indulged them.

So he stuck.

Chapter | 20

(Montefiore Hospital)
3/28/47

Dear Doctor:

I'm quite certain that if reports do not deem surgery necessary, I will not come out too badly in court. There are many points of argument in my favor even though the past is terribly dark and against me. No one in particular is grinding an axe seeking my scalp. So the future doesn't look too dark. Should I get a sentence and if it isn't too large I shall make the best of it. If I should be returned to Court and the gods of fate aren't too severe and parole is granted, I *can't* and *won't let* the *court down,* nor will I *let down* my friends—I mean the ones who I know will support my cause. I honestly and sincerely desire a new life and feel quite confident I *can make good* in spite of the dark past.

Believe me, Doctor Koskoff, I've got too much at *stake* to get into trouble again regardless of my outcome, whether it be surgery or God grants me another chance, just half a chance. I say with deep emotion and from the fulness of my heart, I can't fail again, believe me, Doctor, I can't fail again! . . .

I have always felt a little on the defensive and skirmished in the dark because of a guilty feeling of playing the role of an imposter. Since my life, or the worst phase of it, has been exposed to public airing, I don't feel so much on the defensive. Believe me, my writing and talking about it has done me good—it's sort of a little weight off my shoulders.

My case can become a social success whether surgery is applied or not. With the help of friends I'll irradicate the past. Trust me, believe me. Men like you, Doctor, make me take new interest in life, make me want to prove that Millard Wright has mental qualities that can be turned into channels of honest endeavor. I like to win battles, I should like to prove the skeptics wrong, I should above all else, like to prove to my sisters—to the Forshas and Butlers—that I'm still the leader in daring exploits but in an honest way. To me, Doctor, this would be a crowning success, especially to me because of the terrible, sordid background of crime, crime, crime! Being highly intelligent, you can appreciate the sharp, poignant contrast which would come to me in victory—if the gods of fate permit a triumph.

I love chess, Doctor, and we're playing a game of chess. The stakes are high. Figuratively speaking, I'm checkmated. The move is yours— Your next move is decisive. The public is watching. Some believing, some skeptical, some reserved in passing judgement. It appears to be a test case on some cardinal aspects; it is already a beaten ground on others. I shall play the game to the utmost of my ability in all fairness —I am playing with a man and I know it. I'm going to justify your decision in the final move—we cannot fail and I'm going to be a good actor in real life in an honest role. If I were to go to prison for say 10 years, I would be a broken man on release. Life would have nothing to offer. I prefer death to the prospect of a abject future like this. This present situation if properly managed can be extremely hopeful—I could have much to live for. I want to live!

Humbly yours,
Millard

The newspapers said he occupied a "small private room" in the west wing of the third floor. This wing, completed in 1929, was considered at the time an architectural gem. But it was a gem only to architects. The staff dining room was located on the same floor as the autopsy room. The flow of traffic was inefficient because in 1929 neither doctors nor patients really mattered to architects.

Millard's room, Number 308, like all the others, was equipped with an outer door which could be locked. When that door was open, the room was shielded by two wooden swinging doors, making Millard's guard look like a cop outside an old saloon. To anyone hurrying down the hall these doors were an unexpected hazard since an unwitting patient or visitor could suddenly fling one outward, interrupting someone else's unwary journey.

The room itself was square with tall French windows on one wall covered with a translucent cretonne decorated with flowers faded by thousands of launderings. The walls, pea green, and the floor, light chocolate, were the architect's ideas of relaxing colors. On the wall hung an absolutely irrelevant scene of Venice. Millard occupied a white enamel hospital bed. Two plain chairs and a dresser with a mirror completed the furnishings. A dull overhead light hung from the ceiling.

On the morning they began their work, Koskoff walked into the room to find Millard in animated discussion with the day guard.

"You will have to post yourself outside," said Koskoff sternly. "This patient has a great many psychological and aptitude tests to take. He needs the privacy."

Sheepishly the guard answered, "Outside is my post. We were just talking."

"The day guard's my buddy," Millard said. "It gets lonely in here all day. You know that, Doc."

Buddies they were. Millard was an engaging man and during his stay at the hospital the day guard was not only on the best of terms with him but even anxious about the lobotomy. They never tired of discussing it, the day guard always ending their conversation with a melancholy shake of his head and a sibilant, "Jeez, I hope so, pal. Jeez, I hope so."

The floor nurses liked Millard, too. Ordinarily these nurses were thoroughly professional, not susceptible to any kind of emotional involvement. Nevertheless, they fluttered about Millard. One of the nursing supervisors, gray-haired, starched, and corseted, told Dr. Koskoff, "Put a tall fellow in here with wavy hair, eyeglasses, and a quiet voice, a man who doesn't pinch any of them, and before you know it, this station will be a movie-fan club."

When Koskoff proposed the autobiography, Millard said, "I'm not sure I write that well."

"You wrote for the prison magazines," Koskoff insisted.

"Real writing takes more talent."

"I'm aware," Koskoff said wryly, "that you're no Benvenuto Cellini or Benjamin Franklin or even François Villon. But there is value in the writings of an ordinary man awaiting extraordinary circumstances."

Wright was much too interested in himself to offer more than token resistance. Koskoff knew it and Wright knew Koskoff knew it. His writing helped confirm Koskoff's analysis of his character and personality. His earliest recollections were fear-laden and fear gave way in early youth to a sense of worthlessness. He was unable to form a real friendship. Millard continually regarded others as "coarse" and in these people he continually saw reflected images of his own delinquent self.

There was additionally a confusion as to his sexual identity. Certainly his father, clothing him as a girl, abetted this. Probably one of the reasons he was never homosexual despite the long prison terms was that basically he wasn't interested in sex. Millard had never understood what a significant relationship with a woman entailed. To be sure there were women: Social and environmental pressures assure there will be women. Though women had diseased him, proved faithless, deserted him, he still idealized them. No poetry animated his descriptions. He was searching, he said, "for a woman I could love and would measure up to my ideals." He never for a second thought of a woman in terms of belly, shoulder, bum.

His chivalry, however, was a protective disguise against the shame of sexual impotence. His dreams, invested with symbols of frustration, revealed how poignantly frightened he was of impotence.

Except for Roberta Stuckey.

"She was one of the reasons I tried to commit suicide," he said.

"The suicide wasn't a fake?" Koskoff asked.

"My behavior was a fake," he admitted. "Everything after the suicide was a fake. But when I cut my wrists I cut them because I knew I was in for a long, a very long sentence. And I was ashamed, ashamed of what my sisters would think, of what

Roberta would think. She was the first girl made me figure maybe I wasn't a born loser, maybe I could have what I wanted—a woman, a home, kids, Roberta's kids."

"Who's Roberta?"

"She's a girl I met while I was working at Bauer's. Nothing came of it. But one of the reasons I wouldn't sleep with Ketti was because of Roberta. She wrote me a couple of letters. But then they sent me to Farview."

"You never wrote her?"

"Once or twice. I figured I wasn't good enough for her."

During one of these interviews, Millard suddenly expressed a deep annoyance. "Why do we have to keep dealing with sex? The conversation sounds like jailhouse talk. You're supposed to be dealing with my mind and brain, not my privy parts."

"We deal with it," said Koskoff, "because attitudes toward sex help me understand what kind of man you are. You have certain attitudes toward food: You think prison food diminishes your energy. You have certain attitudes about your body: You are sure the eye defect drives you into crime."

"But they're true," said Millard.

"They are not true at all," said Koskoff. "One of the purposes of these interviews is the hope you will realize they are not true just as one of the purposes is that you'll realize why you didn't sleep with Ketti Wolf Anderson."

"I told you, because of Roberta," Millard insisted.

"You were not in love with Roberta then," Koskoff pointed out. "For that matter you are probably not in love with Roberta now. I think you welcome *her* love and I think you're sorry you're not in love but it wasn't Roberta that kept you off. Your refusal didn't stem from any moral stance."

"I didn't like Ketti," said Millard. "I thought she was over-sexed."

"But you led her on," said Koskoff. "You flirted with her. You gave her to believe you wanted her."

Millard swung away from Koskoff and stonily faced the blank wall. And Koskoff realized he, the doctor and healer, had let the argument carry him away. He had no business delivering truth to this man. Common sense should have told him there are many truths people should never face. There are people by the dozens, hundreds, thousands who cannot sustain life unless they fantasize. Millard was sure the love of a good woman would save him.

The doctor took a deep breath and put his hand on Millard's shoulder. Slowly he coaxed him back to equanimity by letting him talk about how important he was.

Millard had convinced Koskoff he was not a sociopathic personality. It was true that Millard Wright acted out his frustrations against society, that he was self-centered, impulsive, that he appeared shallow. But he had a better-than-average intelligence and he was capable of deep remorse. His behavior was not irreversible. If he was anything, he was schizoid, confused about his identity, distressed over his poor affect quality and the nonviable nature of his personal relationships.

He was, in two words, profoundly depressed. He felt abandoned; deprived in infancy by his mother's death; then by his father's detachment and deafness; later by the marriage and departure of his sisters, his surrogate mothers. Because abandoned, he believed himself worthless. Preoccupied with food and nutrition, Millard was an eternal suckling, equating food with the power to make love and gain ends. Overcome by a feeling of helplessness and a sense of worthlessness, he adopted a veneer of self-aggrandizement. His crimes, striking at society, were a way of diverting his own aggression against himself. But nearing middle age he had run out his string.

Considering this, asked Koskoff, why not a frontal lobotomy?

There was every chance it would relieve or alleviate that profound depression. While Millard's acting out against society let him escape the weary mundane reality which so depressed him, while risk flattered his ego, while theft satisfied his longing for accomplishment, these actions ran contrary to all common sense. They did not fulfill him. The effects he suffered could never sustain well-being nor support a sense of adequacy nor ward off a feeling of separateness.

For there are those whom crime *does* fulfill. They are the real menaces, Koskoff knew, not only to life and property, but to the organization of society itself. Napoleon is, simply, the super-gangster turned politician and Louis Lepke Buchalter of Murder, Incorporated, dispensed more money and patronage a century later and commanded lieutenants more loyal. Bruno Richard Hauptmann because more daring than the aviator whose child he kidnaped and Lee Harvey Oswald's marksmanship plagues the most powerful and cohesive nation on the earth.

This criminal, on the other hand, was severely depressed, potentially suicidal, suffering—for these reasons a human Koskoff could understand, relate to, and pity; for these reasons a man worth saving. Millard wanted to get along and couldn't. The destructive effects of the lobotomy, if there were any; the blunting of his personality, if that did result; would still prove more beneficial and rewarding than what Koskoff suspected Millard would do to himself.

And if Millard and Koskoff were careening toward this operation, so too were many others. The mail piled high on Koskoff's desk. There were letters from everybody—everybody who needed someone for salvation.

. . . I am coming to you to plead for John Virgil, a son of my lifetime friend, Allen Virgil, of Nitro, West Virginia. I have known the parents of John Virgil for better than forty-five years and I never heard of anyone on either side of the house doing an UNLAWFUL ACT, so I know that he did not inherit that kind of temperament from either his father or mother . . . when I read that article about the EMINENT SURGEON it popped into my head that John could be helped . . . The boy is only thirty-seven years old . . . If an operation could restore him it would make him a USEFUL OLD MAN . . .

. . . Having heard so much about your wonderful work in the field of brain surgery, I am taking the liberty of writing to you today in order to acquaint you with my serious problem. My son, Kenneth Swett, is now twenty-five years of age and has spent the better part of the past ten years in prison. Most of his convictions were due to the violation of the narcotics law. Even as a child of five he started with petty thievery which grew worse as the years passed. He had the knack of always, even at the best schools, to find the worst possible friends . . . At this moment he is serving a two year sentence for violating the Federal Narcotics Act. In spite of all his troubles he is a loving and devoted son, extremely kind hearted and good to animals . . . is there any possibility that brain surgery would do anything for my boy? It is needless to tell you how grateful I would be . . .

Koskoff read them all but answered none. Not even the letter from New Kensington, Pennsylvania, the letter from Millard's past:

I am writing this letter to ask for permission to visit Millard Wright. I am told you are the only person who can permit me to see him. I am his former dance instructress and I would like to know if it is possible for me to see him.

It was signed Roberta Stuckey. Millard had never had a dance instructress but Koskoff remembered Roberta Stuckey. Koskoff sighed and laid the letter aside.

Chapter | 2 1

The situation outraged Dr. Edward E. Mayer. Dr. Mayer, a practicing neuropsychiatrist, entertained little faith in lobotomy. Yet it wasn't that David Koskoff was going to perform a lobotomy on a prisoner that was outrageous, it was that Koskoff had not consulted him, Mayer, had not asked his advice, not sought his permission. Dr. Edward Mayer after all was the Chief of the Pittsburgh Behavior Clinic. Jail was his bailiwick. But here it was, a court order telling Dr. Mayer what to do. Without a by-your-leave Koskoff had arranged for a lobotomy on Millard Wright.

Although Mayer was emeritus Professor of Psychiatry at the University of Pittsburgh, although for thirty-five years he had been in charge of the Mental and Nervous Disease Department of Pittsburgh's Presbyterian Hospital and had served as the psychiatrist to the Juvenile Court of Allegheny County, he had yet to admit there was any validity in any of Freud's hypotheses. The son of a rabbi, Dr. Mayer was a Victorian, deeply disturbed by the radical theory of infant sexuality. He was one of the last men in this century to offer seriously the view that sex crimes can be traced to the provocation of a bosom too generously exposed.

Dr. Mayer liked to boast he belonged to the older school of psychiatry. He had made a reputation of sorts by testifying for

Harry K. Thaw, the Pittsburgh millionaire playboy who shot Stanford White atop Madison Square Garden in 1906. Of course Mayer's testimony had been rebutted by alienists sworn by the prosecution but it was they who made a three-ring circus out of the trial, not Dr. Mayer.

A court order was a court order. Dr. Mayer would administer the tests to Millard Wright, but that didn't mean he had to pamper him.

It took Millard Wright two days to realize that Dr. Mayer actively disliked him. Mayer had come into his hospital room, introduced himself, and brusquely described the battery of tests. Millard rather liked tests; he had taken a great many in prison and he was sure he knew his way around questions. He started to tell the doctor that he had a pretty good idea of exactly what each of the tests measured.

Mayer cut him off with the question, "Do you really know what you're doing, Wright?"

"Yes, I do."

"I'm glad one of us does."

Millard trusted doctors. He was positive all of them lived in an interconnecting network of humanity. He was sure Dr. Koskoff had explained the nature of the experiment to Dr. Mayer. Certainly Dr. Mayer would think the experiment worthwhile. But Dr. Mayer thought no such thing, Millard realized. He was abrupt, rude, and patronizing as he administered the tests: the Rorschach, the Wechsler-Bellevue, the Performance Battery, the Hunt Minnesota Test for Organic Brain Damage, the Shipley Hartford for Mental Deterioration, and the Robinson Deliberation.

As he had promised himself, Mayer made it hard for Koskoff. He didn't reply to Koskoff's written requests for results and twice he was out when Koskoff by appointment came to his office. Koskoff finally had to go to Lou Little who asked Judge Thompson to intercede.

Reluctantly Mayer handed over the results.

Koskoff read:

At this meeting the subject was found to be of high average intelligence. The Full Scale score of 107 gave an intelligence quotient of

112 for a person of his age. . . . These quotients are consistent and indicate the high average level. . . . There was a tendency on tests of the Verbal Scale for the subject to respond at first with an inferior answer and by a process of rambling, arrive at an answer of better quality. He was highly motivated throughout the examination, he was persistent, showed good capacity for criticizing the results of his own work and the speed of his response was within normal limits. . . . A comparatively low score on the test of Picture Arrangement indicates some deficiency in the subject's powers in conceptual thinking.

Koskoff scanned through the other tests and read the results of the Rorschach examination:

Although the subject showed no clinical evidence of psychosis following his return from the Farview State Hospital the Rorschach testing showed some residuals of psychosis. There was a marked under-productivity with only 15 responses. His approach indicated a rather empty intellectual ambition, lacking the imagination and creative ability to fulfill his ambition. So strong is this striving toward intellectual achievement that the subject overlooks many of the obvious practical details and overlooks completely the smaller details of his problems. . . . While the testing indicates the subject is of at least average intelligence, his intellectual efficiency is markedly reduced. There is a marked stereotype in both the content of his responses and his phraseology employed. The content is overwhelmingly of the anatomical-sexual character. These responses are related to the subject's concern over sexual matters and probably also to matters concerning his health. They represent anxiety responses as well as furnishing some clues to the beginnings of the behavior which resulted in his hospitalization. . . .

Affectively, the subject has capacities for violent reactions and there is no evidence of adequate control over a tendency toward this type of response. . . . With the meager control the subject has over this potential for aggressive behavior (S-5), it is expected that the aggressive tendencies would be directed more toward his environment than toward himself. . . . His emotional development remains at the egocentric level and his ego structure is so weakened that his perceptions are distorted on a personal basis. At present his capacity for a conforming type of social response is quite limited (P-3). In his thinking he is apt to be rather circumstantial and his judgments are based on superficial characteristics. . . . Thus we have an egocentric subject who is of good intelligence but operating inefficiently and is incapable of mature affective response toward his fellow man and who may, at times, engage in violent aggressive behavior as a reactive tendency.

Which was what Koskoff had already guessed. Millard was perfectly capable of working at the lower levels of a government agency, or perhaps of satisfying the demands of a modest sales position. He could with luck have succeeded as a secondary-school teacher.

A copy of the autobiography Millard was writing was also sent to Dr. Mayer's Behavior Clinic as well as copies of the letters Millard mailed daily. Koskoff himself saw quickly that the more Millard wrote, the longer the autobiographical chapter or the letter, the more distress it revealed. Already Koskoff could visualize the graphs Dr. Mayer would prepare for the inspection of the presiding judge of the quarter sessions. It was all right with Koskoff: The older school of psychiatry had a passion for statistical detail. But the way to find out about Millard, Koskoff believed, was through personal contact, maintained daily, resembling psychiatric sessions.

Not a psychiatrist, Koskoff was still thoroughly familiar with Freudian psychodynamics, having taught it during weekly conferences in organic psychiatry at the University of Pittsburgh Medical School.

He was learning a great deal about Millard. It is true Koskoff may have been learning only that which he wanted to learn, but after every session he left with a hard core of psychological fact and that hard core kept growing, kept tightening, kept convincing him that the operation would be justified.

Chapter | 22

At 4 P.M. on April 14, 1947, Yale David Koskoff met his jury at the County Medical Building. Koskoff knew Norman Ochsenhirt, the committee chairman. Ochsenhirt was a robust extrovert, the only member of this committee still practicing. He was the physician for the Pittsburgh Pirates and he had, almost as a matter of custom, annually secured a box seat for Koskoff and other staff members of Montefiore.

There was no question about Ochsenhirt's sympathies. He admired Koskoff. He had insisted before the ad hoc committee that he be one of the committee men and had insisted strongly enough so that junior physicians yielded to his demand. Two years before, when Montefiore Hospital, in the midst of a reorganization, had endangered Ochsenhirt's surgical privileges, Koskoff, the baseball fan, a member of the Medical Executive Committee, had protected him.

Doctors Charles Gordon and Jonas Rae, Koskoff did not know. They were white-haired men, as wise as senators, officious, obviously used to sitting on committee. The Medical Association expelled from time to time a convicted abortionist, or a doctor who beat his wife, or one who had been legally declared *non compos mentis*. Doctors rarely had to take matters into their own hands.

The courts did it for them. Neither Rae nor Gordon ever remembered denying surgical privileges to a doctor for the nature of the operation he proposed. Nor for describing the technique of that operation. But it was Doctor Edward Mayer, one of four senior physicians in Pittsburgh, who was to bring charges against Koskoff. Though the younger psychiatrists yawned when Mayer spoke in convention, though the forensic experts among them whistled in amazement at some of his legal reasoning, still, he had helped rear this Association. Dr. Mayer remembered other doctors who had bartered their services for livestock and groceries; Dr. Mayer had been on the committee which denied membership to any man not a bona fide graduate of a medical school. Dr. Mayer had seniority.

Koskoff faced his jurors in a vaulted room with a marble floor yellow from age and tread. An echo accompanied his explanations. He was speaking alone in a room used to accommodating a lectern, a microphone, a dais, and several hundred restless, coughing doctors bent on congratulating themselves.

Patiently Koskoff described how Lou Little had approached him, how they both approached Judge Thompson and then Millard. He described the tests he asked Millard to take and offered finally his tentative prognosis for Millard's recovery.

Jonas Rae had a sour look. He searched his committee men's faces and asked abruptly, "What about all this newspaper publicity? The stories in the magazines?"

"I had nothing to do with any of it," answered Koskoff. "I haven't given a statement to anyone, I haven't offered a diagnosis, I haven't promised that I have a remedy for crime."

"Well," pursued Rae, "how did all these stories come to be then?"

"A court action is a public action," Koskoff said. "Whether I am a doctor or not, I can't demand secrecy. An editor is out to sell newspapers. Nothing fits his purpose more than a story about a criminal. That, gentlemen, is the long and the short of it. I never gave out a newspaper interview. I never answered a telephone call which would involve me in a statement. I do not talk to radio announcers."

"Do you think there will be any more newspaper publicity?" Ochsenhirt asked.

"Yes, I am sure there will be."

"Who tells?" demanded Rae.

"A nurse might tell a friend the date of the operation. One of the deputies might have a liaison with a reporter. For that matter anesthesiologists have wives and one of those wives might tell the Garden Club. Who knows whom the Garden Club might tell?"

"Now wait a minute," Gordon interrupted. "What does this have to do with the Garden Club? My wife has a Garden Club. She never discusses my work there. All they discuss is daffodils."

"I think we understand Dr. Koskoff's point," said Ochsenhirt. "He's only arguing that no amount of control that he exercises will guarantee that the public loses interest. And as long as they do not lose interest, they will follow this story."

The three doctors adjourned to a small study.

Ten minutes later, matter of factly, Norman Ochsenhirt read: "While this committee cannot in clear conscience give its imprimatur to the experiment Dr. Yale David Koskoff undertakes, it finds he acts in good faith, that he is true to his Hippocratic oath. Censure is not in order."

Gordon and Rae nodded good night. Koskoff waited for Norman Ochsenhirt.

"Who filed the charges, Norman?"

"Can't you guess?"

"No," said Koskoff, "I can't."

"Dr. Mayer filed the charges. The one doctor who did give a release to the press, which I presume you read."

"I read it," said Koskoff. "I thought it was just a professional opinion."

"I read it, too, and knew immediately that you hadn't consulted him about operating on Millard Wright. That would have been the tactful thing to do," said Ochsenhirt.

"Tactful it would have been," said Koskoff, "but Mayer would have said no."

"His no would have spared you grief. Is it really this important to you, David? This lobotomy? You usually know how to steer a clear course through medical politics."

"Yes," said David Koskoff, "it is important."

Chapter | 23

In the nine weeks that he was in the hospital, Millard had none of the usual visitors most patients see before major surgery. The clinical psychologists who administered the tests helped break the monotony of the day but they had finished with him by the beginning of April. The lone deputy, chair tilted against the wall, was Millard's immediate contact with the world. The nurses passed in and out to say hello, but their visits were brief for he didn't need their attention. The exciting event of the day was Koskoff's visit, but sometimes the doctor didn't appear until late in the evening. Millard liked talking, explaining himself, expatiating, but apparently the doctor was much more interested in the autobiography.

He was overjoyed that he had found Koskoff. He wished he knew exactly what the doctor made of him. Though they talked each day and had gone over his life in detail, Millard still made less of himself than he had before. But Koskoff was a great man and one of the things Millard was proud about was his ability to recognize greatness. He had been reading Carlyle *On Heroes and Hero Worship* and one of the sentences that thrilled his heart was: "No sadder proof can be given a man of his own littleness than disbelief in great men."

On April 14, the deputy let him spend part of the day talking to the two patients in the semiprivate room next door. One of them was named Pat, an Irishman who suffered from phantom limb pain. The other was an elderly, bearded Jew named Ira, who wore his yarmulke day and night. Ira had cataracts.

When Pat asked him, "What in the world do you want out of this?" Millard had a ready answer. He had had a lot of time to fantasize about himself, to hope, and he articulated easily: "I'm tired of living underwater, Pat. I'm tired of wondering if I'll get to breathe again. The operation is going to help me live the way people should. And if I live that way maybe I'll get some of the things I ought to have—a good job, a nice home, a future. I know I'm going to get one thing. I'm going to help make history. Koskoff is going to be world-famous for this and I'm the one who made it possible. So, I don't want to let him down."

That night Koskoff was late. When he came to the room, he said calmly, "Tomorrow is April fifteenth. I want you to prepare for surgery."

"I'm not surprised," Millard said. "I'm ready."

"No second thoughts?"

Millard shook his head. "No second thoughts, Doctor. But here's some favors I'd like. I'd like to relax when I come out of surgery. I'd like to sleep at night without a light. I'd like to take a bath without the guard watching."

"I'll see what I can do," Koskoff said.

Millard rose and opened a drawer in his dresser. "I wrote this letter for you some time ago when I knew I was sure. You can read it now if you want."

"I have three reasons for wanting surgery," it said. "In the first place, if I can't get well and beat the rap, I don't want to live. In the second place, I really want to have a home. You know sometimes I get terribly lonely. In the third place, and this is real, Doctor, I would like to do something for people. Naturally the operation doesn't appeal to me, but I have resigned myself to it and try not to think of it. The thought of it doesn't disturb me as much as it did at first. I have more confidence in you, Doctor, so I'm thinking of it as a success, not a failure."

When Koskoff left, the night nurse gave Millard one and one-half grains of Seconal. In the morning he had only fluids. Some of the nurses dropped in then to tell him how brave he was. The day guard asked if he wanted to send out any mail.

At noon on April 15, 1947, an orderly gave him white pajamas which he would wear to the operating suite. More Seconal. Half an hour later, two orderlies from the operating room brought a cart to Millard's bedside and the drowsy, almost somnolent patient crawled onto it. They wheeled him from the room which had been his home for the past several weeks and as they passed into the corridor, the guard said, "Good luck."

Millard waved back.

In the semiprivate room Pat and Ira came to their swinging door to say godspeed. At the elevator, two young nurses blew Millard a kiss.

He arrived in the operating suite. Koskoff shaved his head lest an orderly make unnecessary scratches. Millard offered no spontaneous conversation. He had some mild "yeses" and "noes" but he was really waiting for the deep sleep the anesthetist would provide.

When Koskoff took the razor to start shaving the scalp, the operation began. Scraping away Millard's hair as he drowsed meant Koskoff was also scraping away some of the features of a distinctive personality. Bare scalp often exposes more than a nude body and it is often a more shocking sight for it always signals helplessness.

The anesthetist positioned Millard on the table and administered Pentothal intravenously.

The operating room was unduly large. While a frontal lobotomy is a serious and delicate operation, it is accomplished with a minimum of attendants, nurses, and assisting physicians. A large circular lamp, four feet in diameter, hung from the ceiling, casting its light on the prone body, the anesthetist, the two nurses, and the surgeon. As Koskoff focused it over Millard, an emptiness came on behind him. The intense glare made it hard to discern with clarity anything not in the light's shafe—the surgical cabinets, the shadowy figure of observant Dan Jamison in the background, the raked viewing balcony, the small oblong windows which lined the room above admitting a minimum of natural sunlight. Now Koskoff concentrated only upon the patient. That concentration always elevates the surgeon out of time and out of familiar space into a bare, remote complex populated only by the flesh and bone beneath him, the instruments which the nurses place in his hand, and the skill, intelligence, and strategy which guide his hand.

The night before Koskoff had determined on a "narrow" lobotomy. A "narrow" lobotomy is less risky than a "deep" lobotomy because there is less bleeding. While no surgeon likes to lose a patient, Koskoff particularly didn't want to lose Millard. Millard's health was good. His life expectancy was long and for the first time he had some expectations. More, the publicity attendant on this experiment had made thousands of people aware of the complexities and dangers of brain surgery. Koskoff worried that if he lost Millard hundreds of people who needed neurosurgery would be discouraged. These were people who needed neurosurgery not for their freedom or reform but for life itself.

The anesthetist stepped back. Koskoff bent to Millard.

Now he didn't even see the green gowns and caps all wore nor the white masks which covered all faces, just his own white-gloved hand and the steel instrument it manipulated and the head beneath him, elevated by a rest attached to the table.

Koskoff placed the grounded electrode he would use for electro-cautery under Millard and bathed his skull with ether, whose powerful odor permeated the room. Next he daubed him with Tincture of Merthiolate, a peach-colored antiseptic. He measured his scalp so he could make his incisions four centimeters lateral to the midline, the coronal suture which traverses the forward part of the skull from temple to temple. He scratched the scalp on the two sides where he would incise. Threadlike lines of blood appeared. With a syringe, he infiltrated novocaine.

The nurses draped Millard and all that was visible now were those two scratches. Koskoff made incisions through the scalp, down one side, then down the other, to the pearly-white bone covering, called the periosteum, the sensitive area which carries the nerves about the skull. Koskoff applied clamps to the galea, which stopped the bleeding, then inserted self-retaining retractors to spread open the lips of the wounds.

With periosteal elevator, a small, spadelike instrument, he cleared through the periosteum to the rock-hard bone. Next the specially designed hand drill—the head circular, three-quarters of an inch in diameter, the edges serrated—delivered two buttons of bone, both of which could be replaced.

This exposed the covering of the brain, gray-blue in color, called the dura because of its toughness roughly approximating that of Saran Wrap. It is sensitive and stretches and when distended causes headaches. Koskoff incised the dura so he could fold it open like a four-pointed star, disclosing the finer filament which wraps the brain, this called the arachnoid because of its spidery threads. Spinal fluid poured from the cut.

Now Koskoff was at the brain itself, its surface and color the consistency and shade of tapioca pudding. Electrocautery stopped the bleeding. He could see the surface blood vessels, the red arteries, and the blue veins. He proceeded to deliver a ventricular needle through this opening which was the size of a nickel. He aimed this long, thin needle on a mild diagonal to reach one of the bases of the skull bone. These bases on both sides support the under surface of the frontal lobes. His landmark was the edge of the wing of the sphenoid, the bone in which the frontal lobes lie nestled. This was the most delicate step of the operation. A slip here into the greater wing of the sphenoid would damage and injure large blood vessels which could result in serious hemorrhage.

First the needle on the right side. An X ray verified its position. Then on the left. Again, the X ray. By following the line of the needle, electrocautery severed the white fibers of the frontal lobes. Simultaneous suction and cautery destroyed the core of this white tissue. Koskoff removed the needle, replaced the dura to cover the injured brain, reinserted the bone buttons in the skull and with interrupted silk sutures closed first the galea, which supports the scalp, and then closed the scalp itself.

It was a routine frontal lobotomy.

Before the doctor finished dressing the scalp, Millard moved. The man was coming back. The nurses, the anesthetist, and the surgeon were shrinking again into ordinary time and space, refocusing eyes, replacing the sterilized surgical instruments, pulling off gloves, the bright arc-light above fading into a glow and then out.

The operation had taken an hour. Koskoff lingered in the room longer than usual. He removed rubber gloves and surgical gown, removed mask and thanked his assistants. But he did not enjoy that flood of relief, that pleasure he customarily felt after successful surgery. Anxiety persisted. There was no elation, no heightened sense of love for those who had participated, no exhaled, "That's that!" only a whispered question, "Now what shall we see?"

And the newspapers had their way once more.

KNIFE TO ERRING BRAIN, said one.

THIEF UNDERGOES OPERATION TO BECOME HONEST, said another.

A third said, "One of the witnesses said Dr. Koskoff was under a terrific strain but he took his time and did a swell job."

Imagine, thought Koskoff that night, a "swell" job.

Chapter | 24

He saw Millard early that evening, paler and less responsive than
expected. Koskoff performed a spinal puncture which made him
more alert. In the morning, Millard was incontinent. Yet when
the nurse asked him if he wanted something to drink, he answered, "Whatever you think." It wasn't until that evening, thirty-
six hours later, that he could answer "yes" or "no" to a direct
question. This was his first and critical achievement in redevelop-
ing his thought processes. Within forty-eight hours he was re-
sponding directly to his environment.

"Well, tomorrow's my big day," his nurse said. "I take my
State Board exams."

"For what?" Millard asked.

"To become a registered nurse," she said.

"You'll pass them."

"Where's your radio?" she asked.

"I don't even miss it. I guess it's in the cupboard."

He was able to sit up and Koskoff asked him if he was ready to
rewrite his autobiography. They had agreed beforehand the true
significance of his life story would lie in the comparison between
the pre- and post-lobotomy versions. Millard tried the next morning, but not then nor at any time during his hospitalization did he

feel capable of this task. Instead, he wrote whatever he chose and submitted these drafts to the doctor daily under the heading "Lessons."

Speech, written or spoken, is behavior. Thought grows with it. Indeed, thought without speech, is inconceivable. But had Koskoff relied solely on Millard's talking, he would have grossly underestimated how dilapidated his thought processes were during the early post-operative period. Millard was able to converse with his nurse and with his doctor and make sense. His writings revealed a greater disturbance.

His ego was disheveled. It didn't know the difference between itself and the id, although before he left the hospital his ego had defined itself and become predominant.

Writing demands mental exploration, a facility in commanding word and thought. To a man with brain damage, a man who can remember this facility but who suddenly feels limited, writing becomes an operation filled with stress and occasionally terror. Psychological defenses protect him in conversation but in writing he must make requests of himself and here he knows to his distress he cannot pretend.

Impotence was a specter to Millard. Sexual impotence always disturbed him. Psychological impotence could prove more devastating. It meant he had to draw upon protective defenses he never knew he had. But have them he did. In finding them, he often used pathetic, half-humorous devices to avoid disclosing deficits; he rarely answered direct questions; he substituted little lies for memory losses. He was enfeebled for a month and his occasional spells of euphoria did not herald bravery or good nature but longings and wishes. Wishes were all he had to ward off depression. Abandonment plagued him more than impotence and here the last ally, his mind, had deserted him.

POST-OPERATIVE MEMO BY DON QUIXOTE   *April 18, 1947*
Montefiore Hospital

A memo report is what is needed in this case. It will determine if the patient is still sick or is just putting it on. Maybe he's putting it on. Who knows? Life is a strange characteristic of characters.

LESSON 2   *April 19, 1947*

Now is the time to come to the aid of their party. Now is the time to come to the aid of their party. Now is the time for all good men to come to the aid of their party [15 repetitions] . . . The American Medical Journal. The American Medical Journal.

LESSON 3   *April 20, 1947*

Gastro-intestinal Surgery—Pediatric Surgery. Gastro-intestinal Surgery —Pediatric Surgery. Gastro-intestinal Surgery—Pediatric Surgery. Pediatric Surgery . . .

Millard mixed up his chronology and often his dates but this was still clinically important in revealing the way speech and thought return to the mind of a brain-damaged man.

LESSON 3   *April 23, 1947*

I'm feeling fairly well today since I got some much needed sleep last night. I sleep pretty good and feel about the same today. So that is why I'm typing a lot today and leaving no grass grow under my feet. OK? The weather looks lovely today. It's so lovely looking that I'm tempted to go out for a stroll. I would if I were on bond, Doctor, providing however, I got permission. Eh?

I should type something but instead I'm running it off verbatim . . . As for originality, Doctor, I have none today. Maybe tomorrow, I'll have a little to dispense with; today, I'm stupid as ever. Stupidity is my slogan now; tomorrow I'll sing a different tune. Let's hope it's a good one.

LESSON 4   *April 24, 1947*

Lesson four constitutes an insanity in itself. I have a strange feeling to commit theft once again if the opportunity occurrs. Do you believe it will occur? . . . What is your opinion? Let's look into the furnace and see if the coals are still warm yet? It might be worth our trouble anyway. . . . I'm only running off the mouth . . .

"Don Quixote," Millard's first signature, is perfect symbolism. Millard always thought of himself as a knight and Don Quixote is a deluded knight. Medically, Quixote is an old man with deteriorating brain cells; it is the addition of the pragmatic Sancho Panza which makes the novel supreme literature. The Don sees the world as it is not. He fabricates heroic deeds and develops

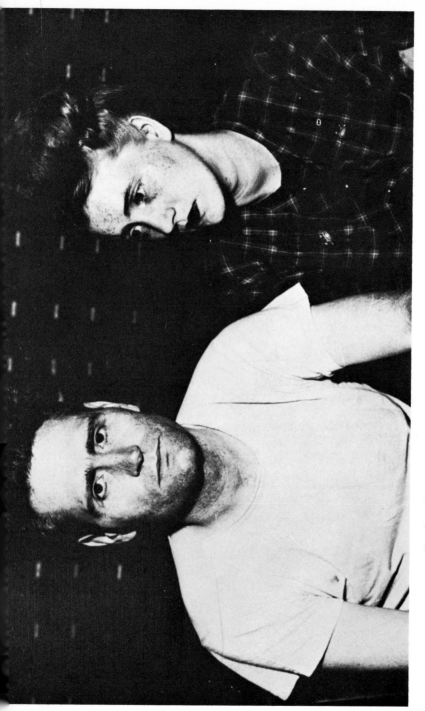

Millard and Roberta Stuckey Wright in the Butler Barracks of the Pennsylvania State Police after their arrest. CREDIT: *U.P.I.*

The suicide notes.

Address all Letters to: Name _Millard F. Wright_ Box A _A-6342_

North Side Station, Pittsburgh, Pa.

Domestic

Information for the Guidance of Relatives and Friends of Inmates:
Inmates are allowed a regular visit 30 days after admission and once every 30 days thereafter.
The visiting hours are 8 to 11 a.m. and 1 to 4 p.m.
No visitors will be allowed Saturdays, Sundays, or holidays.
No books, magazines or newspapers will be admitted unless sent direct from publisher.
No eatables, postage stamps or tobacco will be admitted.
Money should be sent by Post Office Money Order, Registered Letter or by Express Money Order.

JUL 1 8 REC'D

To _Dr. Y. D. Koskoff_ No. _5500 Hobart_ Street
Town _Pittsburgh_ State _Pa._ County _Ally._

Pittsburgh, Pa. _July 16,_ 194 _7_

Dear Dr. Koskoff:

Feeling indebted to you and unable to reward, at this time for your generosity, I have carefully selected a gift — the best I could obtain here — as a token of my gratitude. Your wife will be a better judge of this than either you or I because it falls in a woman's line of "connoisseuring judgements" on home finery. I hope you & the family like it.

I imagine the greatest gift I can present to you is an honest, upright life after prison. I'll do that — have faith in me!

I'm getting along fine. I'm working in the library at present. General health ok. No complaints.

For your information, I'm not bitter over the adverse turn of circumstances in my case. I know this was a defeat to you as well as to me. But as I told you before, I shall take it gracefully and soldier the thing through like a man. Time will tell who's right and wrong on the surgery.

I noticed a few days ago that Time magazine is running an article on me. Did you read it?

You are permitted to visit me. There's no restriction on this. Believe me, it'll be a deep pleasure

Post-operative sample of Millard Wright's handwriting.

May 20, 1952
1526 Monterey St.,
Pgh 12, Pa.
Phone FA-1-9011

Dr. Y. D. Koskoff,
Montefiore Hospital,
Pittsburgh, Pa.

Dear Dr. Koskoff:

My wife's nerves has been on edge considerably, and seem to be growing worse as time goes on. I think that the basic trouble might be too much work and no play. She works five days a week and then on Saturday and Sunday she does the house work too. I help as much as possible, but then that doesn't seem to alleviate the tension. I think she needs a rest.

However, the catch here is that if she takes off from the Clark Candy Co. without a sick leave ok'd by a doctor, she loses her seniority rights in the Local Union. Nowadays seniority rights is tantamount to a job, particularly where a union is concerned. Her seniority rights is very important because it means the job she likes. I wonder why she couldn't get a physical check-up on the nervous tension and fatigue, and above all, could she get a complete physical (she has never had one)?

We're both saving to buy a home and if she is on sick leave, she'll still receive sick pay from the company insurance plan we have, therefore, there won't be too great a loss. Her health and mental attitude is important to my welfare and welbeing, so could we arrange for this checkup? I try to get her to stop chewing her finger nails and being so worked up, but it seems a lost cause. It appears she needs a little medical help in this instance. Doctor, she eats sometimes more than I do and yet seems to have little energy. There is a lassitude or listless ness in her interest in doing things and seems to be tired a great deal. For a girl 27 yrs. old that appears unusual. Her health is up-setting me emotionally and giving me no peace of mind. If she were in good health it seems she should enjoy living and not be so darn melancholy. Please let me hear from you on this matter, it is very important. She has great faith and trust in you. I believe Mr. Mendelson is making progress; however, as to the psychological aspects I'm not sure. Let me hear from you, please!

How's the manuscript progressing? This matter is constantly on my mind. Hoping to hear from you, I am

Gratefully & sincerely,

Millard

Note: We're both covered by Insurance-hospitalization, loss of work by illness, etc.

The final letter written by Millard Wright.

noble attitudes as a defense against the deteriorating self. Precisely Millard's condition.

In the second lesson, the repetitive use of the same sentence is a common symptom in patients with a language difficulty due to brain damage. To understand the meaning of any word is a precious ability. Brain-damaged patients constantly repeat themselves because they fear that in losing the meaning of a word, they have lost the most valuable of all commodities—reality, the grasp on life. The phrase "American Medical Journal" was copied from a periodical inadvertently left beside Millard's bed, but his doctor knew at least he could see words. Whether Millard knew what they meant was another matter. Millard was suffering from word blindness just as Hamlet suffered when he complained to Polonius all he could read were "words, words, words."

By the end of the week, Millard was aware of his loss for he emphasized "stupidity is my slogan." There is no sequence to his ramblings because words had acquired a private, varying meaning. To Millard at this moment, a word not only represented an object but became the object if that was more convenient.

In Lesson Number 5, he wrote, "There wasn't any past—I was born a 'blue' baby." The component parts of his mind were still a salad, jumbled and mixed together. The exclamatory outburst denying a past was a result of that struggle and disarrangement. In the confusion of time without past, Milliard *is* the baby, a sick, depressed "blue" baby.

But beginning with Lesson 6 he began to control the struggle, to quiet it, to find the proper arrangements:

POST-OPERATIVE LESSON   *April 27, 1947*
LESSON 6   *Sunday*

Since this is Babe Ruth's Day, I might as well write about him. Not knowing him too well except what I've heard concerning him, there is very little to say except that I figure he's a swell guy and a boon to sports. The Babe's been a paragon to sports in America. There's been little scandal about him relative to divorce, etc., that one can look back and find his life pretty clean covering many angles socially, and otherwise. Not many sport fans, or sport participants can boast of socially clean records. There is much smudge around them regarding divorce, etc.

Millard remained, of course, a "babe" but this theme of cleanliness suggests a defense against stimulation. Brain-damaged patients with weakened control mechanisms avoid provocative behavior. Tell a brain-damaged man a dirty joke and when he retells it, he will expurgate the obscenity.

On May 1 Millard wrote about the request Roberta Stuckey had succeeded in getting to him:

My girl friend in New Kensington, Pa., has been bothering me about a visit. I told her to get in touch with you and see what can be done. I'm leaving the matter up to you. I suppose you know that the Sheriff's Office don't allow me a visit unless I get permission from you or some official source in command.

So I'm passing the ball to you again. I do this because I know you're in position to pass on the matter without too much difficulty. If we had a bond, this would ease matters considerably. I'd give you a list of people whom I wish to see and you could leave the list at the desk in the office—with your OK on it. That would eliminate the law angle concerning my visits. However, I'm leaving this up to you, but, Doctor, I certainly would like to return to the court room on notification of trial with my attorney rather than to go back to the county jail and wait.

On May 2, he was coping and coping adequately if not politely with reality. He mailed a rudely assertive letter to Louis Little, a carbon of which he sent Koskoff. Without question he was reminding Lou Little and Koskoff that they were obligated to him, that he had done his share, now they had to do theirs:

The Doctor has been wonderful and I wouldn't do anything to embarrass his wishes. Since, however, the operation is over and is a success, I need not hold back anything which might interest our case which I hope can come up next month, because next month is the last month for court trial. I wonder if you might not arrange for my trial for the month of June. If I postpone the case till fall, it's going to be expensive on the county. No need for me to hang around here killing time. We might as well get it over. I think I can get the same consideration in June that I would get in October or November of this year, because if we postpone the case till fall, it won't come up till then. That would be a waste of the hospital's time and ours too. Try to understand this angle. I'm thinking of expenses. Don't misunderstand me, I'm not being kicked out, this move is on my own request because of the July *and August vacation period. Maybe you better get in touch with Dr. Koskoff and visit me to work out some plan of employment for me, for when I come up for trial and am "acquitted" or tantamount to acquittal, I should have a good job in the offing to prove to the Judge that I'm bent on going straight. I'm really serious about this and I should like to work out some program that meets with the Court's approval since the case is disposed of. Please try to see my argument here. I've saved all the money left from the $800 which I gave you. I spent about $70 of the $200. This leaves me enough to get started once I'm freed— which I hope can be arranged without too much trouble and "red tape." If you can't win this case, you better quit the practice of law. I mean this.*

Along with his imagined undernourishment, this debt Little and Koskoff owed him was a subject of which Millard never tired. Three days later, he wrote:

Dr. Koskoff:
Continuing on the subject I finished above, I have this to say. I feel that your responsibility does not cease at the hospital, therefore, what can be done to get me a proper start on the street will be half the battle. I have more faith in you than I do Mr. Little. Courtroom "fanagling [sic]" has cost Mr. Little some prestige; whereas, in your case you have kept your nose clean and retained an appreciable amount of prestige and a good reputation. That is why I have more faith in your interest than in his. Comparisons are odious but in this case I want to be very frank. So that's why I'm passing the buck on to you. You forgot to scalpel the caginess out of me, Doctor. Better have another operation, eh? I'll drop this subject and let you handle the situation from now on, Doctor. However, I might "tab" you with a gentle reminder, if you don't mind.

If the letters were demanding, still Koskoff wasn't annoyed by their tone or their requests. Certainly the lobotomy would change in some small measure Millard's personality, but it was obvious now it was not going to eradicate his juridical sense. Some of his complaints, though exaggerated, had an immediate legitimacy:

I haven't yet had a decent night's sleep because of the nightman's egocentric disposition and selfishness—he's for Mr. Moore and the hell with the patient. A criminal to him is nothing—all that matters in life is his food and his reading. The man's a glutton for food and will die because of it, I mean his life will be considerably shortened because of his weakness for food. I think he needs an operation on his hunger reflexes. This is a little sarcasm for me, Doctor. From 8 P.M. till 8 A.M. the next morning, he continually worries me with his stomach ailments, etc. In the middle of the night, he'll wake me up by turning the lights on to eat. He gets the night help here to bring him up food. Once I'm awakened by such maneuvers, say at 3 or 4 in the morning, I seldom go back to sleep. This knocks hell out of me and I then have to try to sleep the next day. I've put up with this for over six weeks, hoping all the time something could be arranged that might eliminate this nuisance. The night man is the opposite of the day man. The day man is a gentleman cop and tries to be helpful, and let's say thoughtful of other people's rights. Please don't misunderstand me, Doctor, I'm not intolerant with other people, I'm only trying to fight my own battle and I hate for someone else to impose on me when I'm trying to make a comeback.

In some of his letters, Millard confessed a sense of loss: that his memory wasn't as good as it had been, that he couldn't think ahead in either chess or checkers, that he felt he had an IQ of fifty-three with a mental age of five. He never ceased complaining about food. He recited several times the meager diet he had at Farview—potatoes, cabbage, and squash and he was positive his diet at Montefiore would improve his eyesight.

Some days he would discuss topical events with all the pomposity of the uninformed:

May 12, 1947
Monday

I told you I would write on some subject I thought would be constructive and something I knew a little about. So suppose we select world peace. Even though the war has been won at a tragic expense to America, the peace is being lost in chaos of bickering and inconsistency. What defeats the cardinal purpose of the peacemakers today is the deplorable, disorganized condition of the world. Europe and Asia are fraught with disorganization. The industrial and agricultural situation is terrible. It seems that America will have to be the grainery for the world till things get straightened out—and that may take years. So the war expense isn't over yet. Uncle Sam is Santa Claus to the world. The Uncle Sam should be changed to Santa Claus. It seems we're the world banker for wars—we always seem to pay the major part of the bills. The problem is so complex that I dare not suggest any remedy in such a brief statement. Well, we'll let the future iron this out. There's nothing one individual can do. So let's hope and watch.

May 14, 1947
Wednesday

The next president of the U. S. will be Dewey of New York. Why? Because he drew the best poll in the last election and he is the favorite presidential timber in the Republican ranks. The stature of the other candidates doesn't match Dewey. So I'm quite sure that Dewey will win hands down in the coming presidential election of 1948. Wallace is too much of a leftist, while Stassen of Minn. hasn't the Republican support to carry him through to victory. Vandenburg doesn't have a chance, nor does Taft stand a chance at being president yet. Politically, these latter men are small fry and could only win if they were written in on the ticket and had full support of the machine the nation over. Warren of California dropped out of the picture, while Bricker of Ohio withdrew tactfully. The field truly narrows down to Dewey and Truman, unless a third party candidate runs on the independent ticket. Such things are eventualities. It's only rarely that a real, astute states- man gets into power. Back through our nation's history, one can count on the one hand the good presidents. Most men are party machine men and get in because they are backed by the regular party machine; once in a great while an independent candidate manages to get in.

He instructed and discoursed endlessly on all aspects of his case. He wanted to go from Montefiore to the courtroom; he wanted bond; he wanted a sympathetic jury; he wanted to enter a plea of not guilty to avoid detainers lodged against him; he wanted Koskoff to be sure he never said he thought he was in- sane.

Reading Millard's "Lessons," Koskoff marveled at the recuper- ative powers of the ordinary man. Millard, inviolate in his hospi- tal bed, was omnipotent. Left to his own devices, he could have directed armies and parliaments by the third week in May, by which time he was only cursorily bothered by the lobotomy and then only because he didn't dream. Now he was a man again. It was too early for Koskoff to tell if he was a new man or a man who hadn't changed.

Chapter | 25

How long it had been, he didn't know. One morning he awoke realizing this was his room, this was his doctor, this substance beneath the sheets was he himself. He heard the question Koskoff asked: "Who am I, Millard?"

"Doctor Koskoff," he said.

With that answer he realized it was over. He was free, as free as the condemned man who shrieks, screams, struggles to escape until that moment he sees the noose, the chair, or the bullet-pocked wall: he will walk to it, place his wrists placidly for strapping, or hold his head still for the black sack, or shake off the blindfold. He is free because the decision for life is no longer his to make. Someone else has made the decision about existence and once the decision has been made, irrevocable with no appeal, relief is as immediate as breath itself.

Millard was through the terror. He was lobotomized. The fears of diminution might prove true, but he no longer had to worry about them. He didn't hurt but he felt weak and hot. There was a warning within his head, like the warning that afflicts the migraine sufferer: The headache is about to mushroom. The headache never came, but it kept rapping. It continually threatened. He was too frightened to explore his skull with his hands. Later in the day, however, when the nurse got him up to walk, he had a passing glance at himself in the dresser mirror. Two long scars streaked across his head like racers. "I won't look until it's better," he said.

Next he noticed smiles. The nurse smiled, the day guard smiled, Koskoff smiled. The smiles assured him this was *this* world and this was *this* time, an accommodating world, a kindly time. The lightning and volcanoes and eruptions were over.

At a later moment he realized he had been thinking, thinking for days. There was the typewriter on which he had composed his lessons, the newspaper he had read through and discarded the night before, the open book, the page dog-eared. He was taking the tests again, the stern, unpleasant Dr. Mayer uninterested in his answers. The problems were beginning again. He had to finish these tests, prepare for a trial, get well.

This time, the Rorschach result read:

The present testing was made two weeks after the operation and the responses are markedly influenced by the subject's recall of his responses in the pre-operative testing. At times his duplication of the responses was almost verbatim and the subject remarked that it was very difficult for him to see anything that he had not seen before. There is a rather guarded character to his approach at this time. Some important changes were noted. The intellectual approach still emphasizes the abstract superficial type of response reflecting the subject's empty intellectual ambition without the creative ability to fulfill these needs and he still overlooks many important details of his surroundings in his marked effort to solve all his problems as a whole. . . . In the intellectual sphere there has been some improvement in the subject's efficiency which probably is based on reduction of his anxieties as a result of the operation. . . . There is still no evidence of capacity for true insight although the subject clinically shows a superficial insight into his behavior. There is some improvement in his capacity for conformity in his thinking which now approaches the normal range. This does not guarantee, however, the same degree of conformity in social behavior. . . . The subject's anxieties have been lessened considerably from the effective standpoint. The outstanding change has been threefold, the capacity for aggressive behavior has diminished. A tendency toward more passive types of reaction has been introduced and the control of violent aggressive outbursts has been improved."

The analysis of the Wechsler-Bellevue Intelligence Test said:

The subject was retested by Form II of the test and found to be of high average intelligence. The Full Scale score of 113 gave an I.Q. of 117 for a person the subject's age. There was a tendency for the subject to begin with inferior responses and by rambling, arrive at a response of better quality. . . . The subject is still highly motivated toward achievement in the testing and puts forth his best effort. . . . He is clear in his thinking in this test and much more given to making spontaneous remarks about the test itself as well as about irrelevant points, than he was prior to the operation.

Millard suffered Dr. Mayer's rudeness and doggedly kept at his typewriter to finish his daily lessons. Finally he said to himself, "Now it's my turn. Let them keep their bargain with me." Coldly he analyzed the situation. It was he, Millard, who weathered the destructive attack; he, Millard, who faced the outrage of a trial; and he, Millard, who might suffer imprisonment. These men, Koskoff, Lou Little, and even Dr. Mayer, might or might not realize great success. Whether they did or not, still they did not expect outrage, punishment, or humiliation.

The lobotomy kept him from the rage which usually possessed him when he came up against the intractable responses of society. But the lobotomy did not keep him from plotting. There were times he'd gotten his own way even though locked in a cell. Now he wasn't in a locked cell. He was in a hospital with time and convenience to aid his cunning. He wrote Lou Little:

I don't understand why all the publicity about me has died down. The experiment should be more interesting now than it was before my operation. Since you have been acting as publicity agent for the scientific research, you realize additional publicity will not hurt me. I had a plan I hoped to put into effect once I was free, so the better I was known the more chance the plan had of being a success. That plan was to get a job, a good job, to prove that the change had been complete. Now about the trial, if we must have one I want to stand before a jury instead of a judge. A jury of twelve men will render a fairer verdict than a lone judge. There is a warm probability of a "sympathetic" verdict from a jury in the event a trial is necessary. No bond makes this difficult. In addition, not hearing from you makes me worry about the trial. I think this is a situation we should talk over. It would be silly of us to cancel out the experiment simply because we did not plan well.

He gave the letter to the guard who looked it over and supplied the stamp and envelope. "I'll drop it into the box tonight," he promised.

Millard went next door to tell Ira and Pat about the new development he was forcing. It was the last day in the hospital for both. Although Ira was recuperating slowly, he was ever eager to listen to Millard's progress.

While Millard was gone, Dr. Edward Mayer approached, glanced into the empty room and asked, "Where is he?"

"Visiting," said the guard.

"Visiting?" asked Mayer. "What is he, a privileged character?"

"I didn't think it would do any harm. I got my eye on him."

"The man is in confinement," said Mayer. "Did you ever hear of a sheriff who let a prisoner roam around the jail? Every movement he makes gets reported to the sheriff or the district attorney."

"All he does," said the embarrassed guard, "is write letters and take tests."

"The tests go to the district attorney and so do the letters."

"Okay," said the guard.

"When he gets back see that he stays in that room."

"Yes, sir."

In the sheriff's office that afternoon, Mayer, sputtering with anger, said, "I think it's about time Koskoff and Lou Little and Wright realized they cannot turn a criminal procedure into an amusing interlude."

The sheriff knew a message was an order when it came from an appointed official. He took it to heart.

The deputy shackled Millard the next morning.

"Why?" asked Millard. They were old shackles, cast iron with a chain six inches long, irritating to his ankles, heavy, making him walk like a constipated man. "Why?"

"Orders," said the guard.

"Take them off," demanded Millard. "I'm a sick man."

The guard shook his head. "I got the word today. You got the run of the hospital. No more. I can't take them off. The district attorney and the sheriff told me orders. The only order I'm not obeying is to follow you into the bathroom."

"I want my lawyer," said Millard, suddenly desperate. "Call him. His name is Lou Little."

Again the guard shook him off.

"I'll give you one hundred dollars," promised Millard, panic constricting him.

"No," said the guard, the key now in his pocket.

"The Constitution of the United States says that counsel should not be denied a defendant under any circumstance. This is an outright challenge to the civil-liberty rights of Amendment Eight of the United States Constitution."

"I don't know anything about the Constitution," said the guard. "I know your lawyer made a deal with Bill O'Donnell. They'd only see you together. That's the trouble with a deal; it ain't a contract, it's a deal."

"What about my exercise? Koskoff says I have to exercise."

"You're getting a lot of exercise right now, yelling like that," said the guard. He posted himself outside the door.

As Millard suspected, the shackles dismayed the nurses. The shackles revealed to them what he was: a wanted, despised man. Self-consciously they averted their eyes when they made his bed, and hurried quietly from his presence, just as he had known they would. He had known men in jail who refused a visit from their wives with the choked explanation, "I don't want her to see me this way."

Koskoff would have to help him. Even as Millard determined this, the district attorney, in a white rage, was rereading Millard's letter to Lou Little. It was, as Mayer told him, a cheap stunt, a hoax, perpetrated to spring a guilty man. Already the district attorney had decided to remand Millard to the county jail whether Koskoff said he was well enough or not. Already the district attorney had determined no small-time punk would take advantage of his office.

Millard Wright had entered Montefiore Hospital much as a Round-Table champion heroically entered the lists. The radio and newspaper publicity provided his fanfare and there were even sighs from a fair lady to spur him on. He had braved more than any knight. Millard Wright, voluntarily and in absolute possession of his faculties, had undergone unknown dangers to his mind. Resolutely and hopefully he endured anxious hours to fulfill the terms of a curious, desperate bargain he had made with society. Or that he thought he had made. He survived his ordeal. A concept of self appeared after a damaging attack on that very concept. For a while he was a hero, acclaimed by doctors, nurses, and newspapermen. Sixty-three days later he was taken from Montefiore Hospital in shackles and in silence. There was a confusion which persisted not only in his mind but in the minds of others: was he sick or was he evil?

This doubt did not occur, however, to the judge who would preside over his trial. It was not Marshall Thompson, who granted the original petition. It was G. Malcolm McDonald. Lou Little had just finished promising Millard that Thompson would set a reasonable bond and that he would be free until the trial, when in no uncertain terms, Malcolm McDonald made it clear to Lou Little that it was he who would preside over the trial, not Marshall Thompson.

Little asked the judge to set bail. Malcolm McDonald set it at $30,000.

"That would be excessive bail for Al Capone," was Little's shocked protest.

"Why does the defendant think this bail is unreasonable?" asked the stern judge.

"Because I can't possibly meet it," Millard answered.

"The defendant has been in court before. He knows now if he can't meet his bail he has to wait in jail until his trial comes up."

"Your Honor," began Millard meekly, "the bail is important to this whole experiment. You see, if I could meet the bail until the court convenes a jury in the fall, I could prove that the operation has made a different man of me."

"The Court will not reconsider," said McDonald.

"It's a long wait for a man who has undergone a serious operation," argued Lou Little. "The Court knows the defendant will plead not guilty by reason of insanity. Could we move for a trial before the Court adjourns for the summer?"

"What kind of a trial does the defendant want?"

"I want a trial by jury," said Millard.

McDonald shook his head. "Then there's no chance the defendant can stand trial before the fall. This is late May and the Court will adjourn within the next two weeks. That is not enough time."

"You leave little alternative," said Little.

"*I* can try the defendant if he chooses," snapped McDonald.

"I'd like to confer with my client," Little asked, "and give the Court our decision in the morning."

"You will confer now and give the Court your answer or I will move this case over into the fall calendar."

"You mean I can't think it over?" Millard asked.

"The defendant and his counsel have had several months to think it over."

Lou Little shrugged. "We'll plead this case before Your Honor."

Neither Millard nor Lou Little had any idea that Judge Malcolm McDonald had read the letter the district attorney had intercepted—but Malcolm McDonald had. Back in jail, Millard went to work in the prison laundry. By this time, hair covered his scars so the slight sympathy his wounds might elicit from the guards and his fellow prisoners was negligible. The situation left him heartsick. He was even more discouraged when he learned the date of his trial not from his lawyer but from the newspapers. He was a manipulator who out-manipulated himself, a man who always took that extra step.

"You goddamned fool," thought Koskoff when he learned Millard had to stand trial on June 25.

It dawned on him. "We are all goddamned fools," Koskoff said, this time aloud. "Judge Thompson is a fool, Lou Little, Dan Jamison, O'Donnell, and I. What in the world did we think we were doing?"

Chapter | 26

No one likes to be had. The Pittsburgh district attorney resolved he in particular would not be had, not by some dissembling, canny, small-timer who thought newspaper publicity and pity would save him. He asked tough Malcolm McDonald to preside over Millard's trial.

When Judge McDonald asked Marshall Thompson to step down, Thompson did. The older Thompson and the younger McDonald were friends of long standing. When Thompson was the secretary of the law faculty at the University of Pittsburgh, McDonald sat in one of his classes. The two men had begun their practice in the same area of the city. Both had been solicitors for a number of municipalities in the area and now they were both directors of the same bank. This favor McDonald asked was, moreover, a favor Thompson could not refuse.

In 1937, the Republican Party nominated Marshall Thompson and Malcolm McDonald for the Common Pleas Bench. There were four vacancies and Democrats filled the first three, hands down. Thompson ran fourth, besting McDonald by a bare ninety-six votes. A precinct captain in the Fourth Ward discovered one of the voting machines failed to record McDonald's votes. He probably had one hundred and fifty more.

McDonald pursued his interest, consulting anxiously with the County and with the State Chairmen. The State Chairman told him, "If we have to run that election over again, a Democrat's in. You skip it for two reasons. One reason is for the good of the party and the other reason is because you'll get a favor when you want one."

Thompson expressed no doubt as to his colleague's motives for wanting the gavel in Millard's trial. But he was too much of a gentleman, too forthright a man to have suspected McDonald had already reserved judgment.

This is precisely what Marshall Thompson should have thought for McDonald was a desperate man. He had in the past hurt people with a vengeance out of all proportion to their transgressions. Once, as a young lawyer defending a criminal, he heard from a colleague that among the jurors sat a "friend." In open court, without attempting a more discreet solution, he demanded the judge declare a mistrial on the grounds this colleague had planted a juror. McDonald won publicity, and his colleague's professional reputation was damaged irrevocably. McDonald wanted to sit on the State Supreme Court and he was sure any favors he did for the district attorney would forward that ambition.

Marshall Thompson, the grave, austere, much-respected pillar of the community, had abandoned Millard Wright and betrayed Koskoff and Lou Little. He might have argued that a hotel dining room was no place for a court to reach a decision, but Koskoff and Little understood him to mean the Court *had* reached a decision, that if Millard Wright did this, the Court would do that, that that noon in the hotel dining room they were discussing a *quid pro quo*. Koskoff and Little were fools not to have asked for the binding court order, the guarantee positive. But they didn't suspect then that Marshall Thompson, for reasons of personal expediency, would walk away from a man he had allowed to damage himself. They could argue, too, with Millard, argue until they were blue in the face, that it wasn't their fault but Millard would always insist deep down that he, the victim, was the only one who didn't fink.

Millard was running into bad luck with his judge. Nor had he helped himself with Dr. Edward Mayer, Supervising Director of the Behavior Clinic of the Criminal Court in Pittsburgh, who would appear at the trial as *amicus curiae*.

In jail, Millard lost his temper with Dr. Mayer.

"What type of a plea do you propose to make, Wright?"

"I haven't consulted my attorney yet so I don't really know."

"You must have some idea," Mayer pursued. "You underwent a lobotomy. Isn't it going to figure in your defense?"

"Are you interested in my line of defense because you're a stooge for the D.A. or are you interested in the operation as a psychiatrist?"

What Wright didn't know was that the District Attorney had commissioned Dr. Mayer to make a full report on Millard Wright for the presiding judge of the Quarter Sessions. The report was "privileged communication"; neither the defense nor the prosecution could examine its findings. It contained a detailed account of a battery of tests performed by a clinical psychologist, and clinical impressions, fleshed out with correspondence with leaders in the fields of lobotomized subjects.

Millard stood trial on June 25, 1947, in the Allegheny County Courthouse, waiving his right to a jury. Koskoff arrived early. The courtroom was empty. The court was an old musty one. The jury box, the bench, the tables were worn and scarred. On the walls, staring down like a phalanx, were a series of portraits of the venerable, bearded judges who had sent men to prison or to freedom from this room. The faces bore an amazing similarity to one another.

Inside, the first man Koskoff saw was the tall, slender William O'Donnell. O'Donnell had been a court reporter in his younger days. He had lent his efforts to this case because he wanted to see a good story live and grow. O'Donnell was a gentle, kind man. This morning, in his dark-blue suit and subdued tie, he looked more the honest hardware salesman about to stammer he didn't subscribe to capital punishment than an aggressive prosecutor. His voice had the soft lilt of the movie Irishman and there was no rasp in it when he cross-examined witnesses.

Lou Little came down the aisle and pushed through the gate that separated the public from the courtroom proper. Lou swaggered into a courtroom much like a heavyweight champion swaggers into the ring, sure he is the worthy focus of all the noise and clamor of the auditorium, a man who cannot wait to get going. Lou always wore expensive, custom-tailored suits, brilliant white-on-white shirts, cuff links which gleamed with diamonds, and a necktie proclaiming his presence like a siren.

The court rose. Judge McDonald mounted the bench. Nervously Millard rose at his table with Lou Little. Unblinking, Judge McDonald heard the charges read and then, and only then, did he fix a hard stare upon Millard.

"Does the defendant understand the charges?"

"Yes, sir."

"Are you represented by counsel?"

"Yes, sir. Mr. Little is my lawyer."

"How does the defendant plead?" asked McDonald.

"Not guilty by reason of insanity," answered Lou Little.

At last the judge blinked. Just once. Then he nodded to William O'Donnell, who began his prosecution.

Dr. Mayer's testimony was damaging. He testified that Millard had carefully planned the robberies which ruled out the possibility of irresistible impulse; that Millard had fallen in love with a Roberta Stuckey, which gave him a motive for the robberies. When Lou asked Dr. Mayer whether Wright wasn't once adjudged criminally insane, Mayer replied he was adjudged criminally insane because he attempted suicide, not because he attempted burglary.

During this testimony, Wright tugged at Little's arm and whispered fiercely. Several times Lou held up his hands placatingly. Once Millard made a fist and banged on the table. When Mayer stepped down, Millard regained his composure, staring intently and seriously at the other witnesses who succeeded to the witness chair.

It was hard to believe he was the desperado whose fate they were discussing. He looked more like an impoverished scholar. His suit, neatly pressed and cleaned, was old and just beginning to fray at the sleeves. His shirt was new but the tie was second-hand and his shoes were unshined. Yes, he was the man who buried himself in books, neglecting his appearance because vanity distracted him. He sat rigidly through the rest of the testimony, a bundle of electricity waiting to expend itself.

The attitudes of the people within the courtroom became electric, too—emitting charges of pity and hostility. The spectators sat deeply curious, occasionally mesmerized by the psychiatric testimony. They had come fascinated by the prospect of punishment. But they lost their vicarious selves as they, too, began to grope with the profound concept of what is sanity and what is insanity.

The jury box, to Millard's left, was filled with other prisoners awaiting disposition of their own cases. They were a shabby, tatterdemalion group, a ragamuffin jury whose desire for the defendant's victory flushed the court. Although they were attentive and quiet, several times McDonald turned to stare at them as though they were rowdy intruders.

Koskoff was the last witness for the defense. He followed Dan Jamison, who testified Millard Wright was insane at the time he committed the specified burglaries.

In his hand, Koskoff held a plastic model of the human brain. Lou started him off. Koskoff balanced the model and began to describe the cerebral cortical areas, turning as he did to face the judge. For the first time, Koskoff noticed McDonald's left hand was flaccid, in paretic posture. McDonald had a left hemiplegia. A visceral ache stabbed the doctor. The plastic model seemed suddenly heavy. He was able to talk carefully, clearly, cleanly—these were lessons he had delivered over and over again to colleagues, interns, and nurses—but he felt estranged from his own words. There was a terrible pathos here. Koskoff was patiently explaining a brain-damaged defendant to a brain-damaged judge and he knew there was no sympathy, no chance of understanding between the two.

William O'Donnell on cross-examination asked, "What do you think the results of this operation will be?"

"I think Wright will do well if he is given favorable employment and environment," said Koskoff.

"If he is released do you think he will still be a thief?"

"I don't think he will, but there's nothing in surgery to guarantee a definite result."

"Just what would your recommendation be?"

"From a humanitarian viewpoint as well as that of a citizen I think he should have his second chance. And so should we."

"We?" asked O'Donnell.

"Wright undertook a dangerous mission which is payment of sorts for his crime and we—and I mean you and I—ought to have the chance to confirm if the mind of the criminal has vanished and the mind of a man to be trusted has appeared."

"Have you any more specific recommendations?"

"Psychiatric supervision for the next year or two. This should give us a clear picture as to whether his criminal tendencies have been removed."

"Could we get that picture just as well in jail?"

"Jail," Koskoff answered "is not a normal environment. If I thought for a minute you were intent on returning Millard Wright to jail, I would never have undertaken this operation."

With that, the five-day trial adjourned, neither Lou Little nor O'Donnell summarizing. McDonald promised to read his verdict the next day, June 30.

That afternoon, in his study, he read the testimony and reread Mayer's report, with particular attention to Mayer's conclusions:

Clinical Impressions:

In the clinical, as well as the psychometric studies there have been noticeable changes in this man's responses. He is much more alert than he was formerly and there is a much greater warmth to his personal responses in the clinic situation. He gave the information spontaneously that he now has considerable difficulty in playing chess while he formerly was the jail champion in this game and could plan his game four or five moves ahead as well as anticipate his opponent's plan of attack. He is now unable to plan his moves very far ahead. While this observation may be the result of his rather extensive reading about personality changes following lobotomy, it is interesting to note that it follows the pattern of reported cases as well as the reduction in his ability to handle the Deliberation Test—Numbers. During several interviews following his return to the jail the subject has confirmed his egocentric outlook on life and his capacity to distort the full facts that are important in the diagnosis of his case. This tendency is strong enough to throw serious question on his ability to give a truthful statement at any time. . . .

In conclusion may we state that your Behavior Clinic as an agency of the Court interested in forensic and social psychiatry has as always been impartial in the subject material before it. We have tried in this report to summarize the data relative to the prisoner as well as the literature available from authentic sources. We do not find any material or important differences in this individual's personality as it presented itself to us previous to operation. He has not suffered any important decrease in learning ability. He has no changes in intelligence level. He does show less tension. There is apparently some difference in his affectivity or emotional tone. He seems to be more responsive in the interviews. However, we cannot find any change in his personality pattern that would convince us that there have been any material changes in his anti-social tendencies.

The next morning, the judge began reading aloud while Millard stood trembling before the bench. He detailed Millard's criminal history, his attempted suicide, his record at Farview, the history of the lobotomy, and the testimony of Millard's trial. McDonald found that Wright was legally sane at the time these burglaries were committed and that therefore he was adjudged guilty. He paused. McDonald had pulled the pin on the grenade; now he threw it: "We suspect many people will be willing to take the chance in this case in the hope that society as a whole might profit by learning whether or not such a lobotomy operation can cure a criminal of his criminal tendencies. However, we do not see how this court can take this chance in a case of this kind. We feel that if we were to accede to the request that Wright be absolved from incarceration for the crimes he has committed and for which he has been found guilty that we would soon be overwhelmed by similar requests from many other habitual criminals who are now incarcerated and who would be willing to submit to similar operations if they felt such operations would free them. We have given much thought to the question of disposition and we feel the only proper disposition of the case is to impose sentence on Wright and to give him credit for the time he has already spent in jail and in the Farview State Hospital and in Montefiore Hospital while undergoing this operation and some additional leniency for his having submitted to the lobotomy."

It was a literate, thoughtful, and perhaps appropriate decision. Koskoff could have argued it was specious reasoning for McDonald to suppose the neurosurgical clinics of the country would be inundated with requests from prisoners for lobotomies. It is a matter of history that no criminal has been lobotomized since Millard Wright nor has any criminal requested such surgery.

Judge McDonald wrote his decision in the depersonalized atmosphere of his study. The tone of that decision was modulated in sharp contrast to the outburst McDonald could not restrain the day of sentencing. Brain damage weakens behavioral controls and personal interaction irritates that weakness.

Lou Little started off by offering an impassioned plea for leniency.

"This man must be punished," McDonald interrupted. "He or somebody thought up this idea of a brain operation . . ."

"I suggested it," said Little. "That's a matter of record."

"And the sole purpose behind it was to help your client evade sentence," snapped McDonald.

"Your Honor, my client underwent this operation in some part to further science."

McDonald snorted. "If this operation was in the furtherance of science, why all the publicity? That's all it was. A cheap publicity stunt."

"I resent that," Little said.

"Well, that's what I think. You admit it was your idea and I still say it was all for publicity. It reads like the story of a dime-novel surgeon."

"Are you talking about Dr. Koskoff?"

"I'm talking about Doc Savage in the pulp magazines. That's what this operation reminds me of. I have no confidence in such surgery. Hopes perhaps, but no confidence. This man is a habitual criminal. And I sentence him to two to twelve years."

Ashen, Millard stood numbly through the whole proceedings, his hands behind his back. When McDonald gaveled the sentence, Millard almost toppled forward. A bailiff supported him, as McDonald rapped again and again to quiet the expostulating Little.

"I go to prison with no bitterness of heart," Millard wrote

Koskoff. "It is my humble purpose to prove that rehabilitation is certain with or without prison. I shall not be dramatic or erratic. Give my respects to your wife. To a fine guy who did a great kindness in an hour of need. I salute with humility and gratitude. You were superb."

Chapter | **27**

Three months later Judge Malcolm McDonald left his home at 5150 Beeler Street for a Sunday morning stroll. At noon, a casual visitor heard the car engine coughing in the garage. Entering, he found McDonald slumped behind the wheel. A vacuum hose was attached to the exhaust and the judge had squeezed it through one of the ventilator windows after winding up all the others. On the seat beside him·were two empty water glasses and a large number of packets which had contained sleeping tablets.

The police of the Squirrel Hill district who answered the call administered oxygen for more than an hour, but Judge McDonald never revived. Hospital tests that afternoon proved carbon monoxide the cause of death. McDonald's family physician told reporters that Judge McDonald had suffered poor health for the last three years. McDonald was fifty.

The penal code of Pennsylvania lists suicide as a "grave public wrong" and it describes suicide thus for the same reason the psychiatrist reasons that the blow inflicted upon the self is symbolically intended for someone else. Suicide punishes people—wives, husbands, daughters, sons, friends. Lou Little and Koskoff could not help but relate Judge McDonald's suicide to Millard's punishment.

"I can give you a pretty good answer about Millard Wright and Malcolm McDonald," said Koskoff.

"What is it?" asked Lou Little impatiently.

"When McDonald was trying Millard Wright he was probably holding silent inquiry into his own case."

"That's pretty good," said Little. "No psychiatric mumbo-jumbo."

"Thank you," said Koskoff ironically. "Except it's not mine. It's from Joseph Conrad's *Lord Jim*. It's why the self-satisfied Brierly commits suicide."

"You know something, David," said Little, rising, "you read too damn many books. I never never trust a man who reads books. Gives him a conscience."

"Why do you distrust men of conscience?" Koskoff asked.

"A man with a conscience changes his mind," said Lou with finality.

It was one of those statements that stays forever with a man. Koskoff saw much of Lou Little during the next decade. They belonged to the same temple. They knew the same friends. They could talk. But with this difference: Now they understood each other. Koskoff understood that Lou could abandon not only people, but even the truth, with an imperious disregard.

After Millard's sentence and Judge McDonald's suicide, Lou Little went on to greater influence at the bar and in Pennsylvania politics. In fact, he was the toastmaster on one occasion when a bar association presented a Patek Philippe watch to Marshall Thompson. Koskoff pursued surgery, in time to become one of the best-known neurosurgeons in western Pennsylvania.

These events sound continuous but of course they weren't. We live in an episodic universe and most things burst upon us. Millard's imprisonment remained sequential for Koskoff and Little because Millard wrote to them from time to time, made demands upon them, persevered in these demands until they dared not refuse him. Millard simply would not disappear from their lives. In prison, Millard did not despair as these two expected he would. He exerted himself constantly to win parole. He remained a presence in the daily life of Koskoff and Little, a figure recalled once a week, sometimes once a day, a puzzling Bartleby the

Scrivener, still in his corner, still looking at his blank wall, still somehow making his leaden personality into a basic, brooding plea.

It was during Millard's hospital stay that Yale David Koskoff learned his wife, Elizabeth, was dying of diabetes mellitus. When she did succumb, she left him with two small children to raise. Two years later he married Betka Schram, the nurse who had assisted him in all his operations.

On the day they were married, several Pittsburgh papers were correct in the color of the bride's dress, in the schools she had attended, in the names of the bridesmaids and where the bride and groom would spend their honeymoon. All the papers reminded their readers that Dr. Koskoff was the surgeon who had operated on Millard Wright to cure this criminal of his antisocial tendencies.

Part Three
THE LOSER

Chapter | 28

Koskoff gave Millard a pair of eyeglasses before he went to Western State Penitentiary. The glasses were ground with unusual precision in the hopes they would compensate for Millard's congenital defect. This new prescription, Koskoff felt, might well ease the constant strain. Koskoff's other parting gift was an old typewriter. Millard promised to write every two weeks about his general progress through the post-operative period. He accepted these gifts with a gratitude that was almost slavish. Friendship was not Koskoff's controlling motive, nor was pity, but certainly Koskoff felt an incipient concern that in someway, despite good intentions, he had contributed to Millard's punishment.

By July 4, Millard had passed through quarantine, was assigned a cell, a number, and a routine in the prison library. He slipped into the ever-filtered current of prison life. By the time he wrote his first letter to Koskoff he knew the names of all the Parole Board members and their customary practice, including the "holdover" policy. Other prisoners told him there was every chance the Board would keep him in prison longer than his minimum sentence because he was a repeater: the Board subscribed to progressive punishment and Millard had all the time in the world to mull over this unpleasant prospect.

His cellmate was an alert bank embezzler named Gerard Hamilton. Hamilton believed his only mistake was not preparing for a surprise audit; Millard believed *his* mistakes were in not electing a jury trial and in writing a letter which cast suspicion on his operation.

"And the trouble was I *knew* I was wrong in going before the judge, letting him sit alone. I *knew* it. I was just impatient."

"Why were you wrong?" Hamilton asked. "How could you know the judge had made up his mind? How could your lawyer know that?"

"Do you know anything about judges?" Millard asked, off on one of his socratic careers. "A judge knows his own mind. Twelve men do not. Every con will tell you, if you didn't do it, you want a judge. If you did, you want twelve men. Twelve men can go crazy in a locked room."

"You got a bum deal," concluded Hamilton.

"Well," said Millard, "I knew what I was doing."

"Yeah," said Hamilton, "you knew what you were doing. There is no trouble in this world like the trouble you get when you know what you are doing."

There was a significant change in Millard's demeanor. He had no bitterness. His sentence was a blow he had not expected; his friends in prison thought it was a low blow, but Millard dwelt on it matter-of-factly. It was something that had happened, spilt milk over which he wasted no tears. He noticed, too, that he rarely became angry. In the past, prison always meant a seething rage once a week. He would flare up at a guard's command or over some pointless directive from the administration and there was always a personality to irritate him. During his stay at Western State, however, he never lost his temper. For the first time in prison, he gained weight, twenty-two pounds in all. If nothing else, he could take a cold, remote comfort in realizing his lobotomy helped him adjust to the rigors and meaninglessness of prison.

Bitterness could have preempted his existence and corrupted his reform. His cellmate and other fellow prisoners told him he had been wronged, that society owed him something. Yet their fierce sympathy, their sense of outrage at his predicament never goaded him into aggravated behavior. Within two weeks of the start of his sentence, Millard, who had once been the prison legal expert, became instead the medical expert, knowing all there was about the new techniques, revealing to all the convicts the spectrum of the medical horizon.

He read psychology books omnivorously, from Behaviorism through Gestalt, complaining constantly about the paucity of technical and professional volumes in the prison library. He was the disciple of all schools. Koskoff subscribed to several of the professional journals for him but even their statistical mumbo-jumbo and their exotic argot didn't lessen his enthusiasm.

He took to attending Protestant services every Sunday and Bible classes every Wednesday. It was a curious departure. He was a sincere religious skeptic. And church attendance in prison often marks a man in the eyes of his fellow convicts. Jails contain a high proportion of sex criminals. A sex offender to a burglar, a murderer, or a thief is an untouchable. No sooner does the law pack a rapist or an incestuous father in a cell, than he will make for the chapel, Bible under his arm. While there are other reasons convicts do not attend chapel, the wish not to associate with sex criminals is the one they always profess to the chaplain.

It was, however, no sudden wellspring of religion which bubbled within Millard. Intuitively, he sensed that Reverend Stremal and Father Huber could help him win a parole. Millard was a man who had sacrificed and he knew in the eyes of these two clergymen he was more than the ordinary felon, more than the ordinary criminal. Nor did the other prisoners scorn him for his devotions. He was an anomaly: a man who didn't belong behind bars with them. Convicts do not discipline or ostracize an innocent man or a man unjustly imprisoned. They protect him. That he must share their time is enough.

Besides, they liked him. Millard wrote their letters and drafted their legal briefs. Letter writing is a valuable skill in a place where the majority cannot articulate. A man who can write a coherent letter, prepare an adequate petition not only wins gratitude, which can be transformed into favors, but he makes money. While wardens and prison administrators assure legislatures and visitors that prisoners trade only in scrip or credits, there is no place in this world where money doesn't circulate, least of all in prison among men who have a certain gift for covert activity.

Though Millard's memory returned, as well as his facility at chess and checkers, he worried constantly. He was possessed by the idea of a parole. He learned early that he would have to serve four and one-half years of his sentence before the Board would hear his case. The Parole Board also informed Millard that the time he had spent at Farview, in Montefiore, and in awaiting trial did not reduce this. The Board explicitly told him he would have to serve his twenty-three months over again.

He filled his letters with this complaint. He asked Koskoff and Lou Little to help. While he was perfectly capable of asking the Court to credit these twenty-three months as legally incarcerated time, as the Court had stipulated, he dreaded doing so. He wrote:

> My hands are tied. I know I have sound reasons to go to court and ask for my legal rights but if I do and even though I win, I would lose. Why? Because the Parole Board would be angry and in revenge would hold me over my minimum for several years on grounds of an anti-social attitude and past criminal history. The Parole Board has the power to make me do twelve years if they want to be vindictive and implacable. Realizing all this I have bowed and humbled myself as if I were a lackey before his majesty's will. I've been very cooperative and am endeavoring to build a constructive picture here in the hope that you and Mr. Little will not let me down. I am not pleading with you for selfish reasons. You two as scientists owe it to yourselves to facilitate my means of freedom so that this scientific research may have a decent and proper opportunity to function.

In consecutive letters, he kept begging Koskoff to persuade his medical colleagues to fix things, to pull wires. He always repeated the names of the warden and the members of the Parole Board. Often his letters deputized Koskoff to explain the situation to Lou Little.

Lou Little eventually filed for the writ and the Court after due deliberation ruled in Millard's favor, adding the twenty-three months as time served.

More placidly now Millard began to take in his surroundings. He worked in the library, a post which let him meet many more of the convicts than he would have met in the cafeteria or the laundry or the machine shop. All of these men knew him. His story had gained wide circulation. On more than one occasion, a prisoner came into the library, went through the process of filling out the card, just to talk to Millard, to see what this medical prodigy was.

Millard lorded it over these men. Their curiosity was tempered by sympathy and awe. Millard could spot them right away and he would indulge himself in a long discourse about the prospects for neurosurgery and the inequities in the law. They dared not interrupt him. He could turn from them, haughty and superior. He was able to cut, to bruise feelings. "Here's your book," he would say, "on your way."

"Now what the hell is wrong with you, Wright? All I did was ask a question."

"An uninformed question," Millard would reply.

He would talk to the prisoners who checked out Aristotle or Hawthorne, Freud or Shakespeare but he was uncharitable to the men who wanted Zane Grey or Floyd Dell, forgetting he, too, once had unsophisticated tastes. When they innocently asked him, "What's a good book to read?" he would often as not maliciously pass them John Stuart Mill or Montaigne, writers they couldn't begin to comprehend or enjoy.

He spent much of his time formulating his own book. It was a fantasy but Koskoff never abused it. In letter after letter Millard planned every contingency except the book's composition. He wanted to know whether Koskoff was interested in reading over the manuscript? Would Mrs. Koskoff help with the typing? Would the medical faculty at Pittsburgh certify his book's accuracy?

On the anniversary of his lobotomy, he wrote: "As to mental or personality changes since the lobotomy—they are as follows: pronounced decrease in future apprehension; marked change from quick temper impulses to normal moderation; increased scope of interest in local and national happenings and greater breadth of development in emotional maturity."

The court order Lou Little obtained meant Millard could reasonably plan on parole sometime in the late winter of 1949. That delivery invested all his correspondence. He needed a sponsor and he asked Koskoff. "I prefer you instead of Lou because it is possible that the Parole Board will think my lawyer is actuated by a desire for money. But they will believe you about the experiment."

"He thinks of all the angles," Lou said. "It's all right with me. But let me tell you, sponsoring a parolee isn't that easy. He's got to have a job and he's got to have a place to live before he gets out."

"Couldn't you give him a job?" Koskoff asked.

"Doing what?" Lou asked. "Reading law?"

"What about some kind of clerical work?"

"His eyes, David. Remember? His eyes are going from bad to worse. He can't put in eight hours reading. Can you use him over at your place reading X rays."

Koskoff admitted he couldn't.

Sponsoring Millard wasn't as simple as Koskoff thought. He couldn't simply sign his name to a blank form and trust to the efficacy of an impersonal organization to process the application. He had to guarantee Millard a job and he had to guarantee Millard a place to live. Suddenly Millard wasn't a patient anymore, a man who would or would not get well; in either case with someone else to take care of him or take care of what families euphemistically call "arrangements." Millard was now someone of whom Koskoff was frightened. He didn't fear harm for himself. Koskoff had two young children. Millard wasn't the man Koskoff wanted to bring into his own home, even if he needed a majordomo. With a start, Koskoff suddenly realized Millard was not a nice man. Millard was too smart for his own good yet not smart enough.

The telephone would get the man a job, Koskoff thought. It did not. There weren't jobs to go around. As if this were not enough, Millard was not only a convict, but a lobotomized convict, sure to attract publicity when he went to work. Also Millard had an exaggerated opinion of what he could and ought to do. After all, he was into his forties without skills of any kind. His intelligence distinguished him in prison—on many occasions the other inmates called him "Professor"—but a professor in the real world has a Ph.D. In one prison, he had learned bookbinding. When Koskoff asked about his bookbinding skill, however, Millard ruefully admitted it was self-taught, his methods antiquated and expensive and that here, too, a vocational director at the prison told him there was only a limited need and the need was for artisans of proven worth.

So much for his executive and manual skills. There it was. Millard had a repugnance for his criminal past. He wanted a reward for being a reformed Millard and the reward wasn't in the cards. At least Koskoff couldn't find it there.

Koskoff had to stall Millard as other men stall creditors. To-morrow. Soon. I'll get to it tonight. Don't worry. The delay fed Millard's anxiety. He became the importunate man, the scoundrel with a case whose lies have long ago discouraged the squire, the Billy Budd blessing Captain Vere, the man in a cage whose last weapon is the postage stamp.

Now it was March. Koskoff had agreed to sponsor him. But Koskoff could not find him a job. Millard tried to tell the Parole Board that Dr. Koskoff was an important man, a man with con-nections. Lou Little was an important man. Surely they all had heard of Dr. Koskoff and Lou Little. There was a picture in the paper of Lou Little with his arm around Alben Barkley, the Vice-President. They could get him a job. Give them another week.

But that March, the Parole Board turned him away. A sense of worthlessness assailed him for the first time since the lobot-omy. He had spent a lifetime bringing out the worst in himself and he was apparently able to bring out the worst in others, elicit it, prompt it, provoke it, and suffer for it. How hard was it, Mil-lard asked himself, to be a friend? He could not bring himself to answer his question. He would not think about it. It never oc-curred to him that indeed it is often hard and most men tolerate the onus because friendship is give and take, help and be helped, it is laughter and sympathy. It is not a joint project, agreed to in a sterile room. Millard never saw that there has to be a *reason* for a friendship and that that reason has to be a part of the past worth preserving and something in the future still delightful to en-counter. He was demanding that Koskoff play the saint. For sev-eral sad centuries sainthood has been an underpopulated profes-sion.

In September, Father Huber found Millard employment at Mercy Hospital in Pittsburgh.

In a letter dated October 11, 1949, Millard wrote Koskoff: "I received a reply from the Parole Board to the effect that my discharge date is Saturday. I am glad a final decision has been rendered."

In looking over his correspondence, his doctor, the objective man of science, read an impressive behavioral document. Millard's writing style in the last twenty-eight months achieved tension and buoyancy even when his content was banal and repetitious. What struck Koskoff was how filled his letters were with legal strategy and plans, how detailed and important were the goals he set; yet once the Parole Board gave him his freedom, there was no jubilation, no pleasure, just a stark statement of fact that on Saturday he would be released.

Chapter | 29

The warden recited the usual sing-song litany about behaving himself. By noon Millard was outside the stone gates of Western State Penitentiary, waiting for the North Side trolley. It was a clear fall day, the air pure oxygen, the October gusts thrashing the few leaves from the trees.

In a canvas shopping bag, Millard carried his personal belongings: the typewriter, which for the past months had lacked a ribbon; a book by Wolfgang Köhler he had bound himself; some underclothes; and his correspondence tied in a packet. He wore his only suit which smelled from camphor and was more ragged and soiled now than when he had worn it at his trial. He had $29.50 in his pocket purse.

The trolley pulled alongside him, slipping to a halt as sparks flashed from under its wheels. The street noises, the bright sun, the gaudy day, the yellow trolley with its different smells made him nauseous. He paid his fare and stalked to the last seat, sitting alone preoccupied with freedom.

North Avenue was exactly what he expected: a row of run-down, unpainted dwellings, the steps leading to the stoops, rickety, the banisters often lolling, broken, or rusted away from their supports. Many of these dilapidated buildings were whorehouses and the doorways, the porches, the windows were blank, deserted —a street perpetually waiting for night.

When his landlady opened the door, Millard's heart began pounding. She was a pleasant, elderly widow who often let rooms to released convicts.

"You're on the fourth floor," she told him.

Millard followed her up a stairway covered by a threadbare carpet, in many places worn to the backing. A gerrybuilt wall had made two rooms out of one but had not evenly divided them. The window, forever locked in place by many coats of enamel, was quartered, and one pane had a long crack. A limp red curtain afforded privacy, but it was musty and brown stains dotted it. There was a single bed with a brass headboard; an easy chair with the stuffing beginning to pop; a wooden bureau, the knobs black from countless fingers; and a mirror with nonreflecting patches where the mercury had worn away. A lamp with a bent shade hovered over the chair. A corner sink projected from the wall, obscured by a rickety screen. Millard could see a roach dart for the drain. The bathroom was in the hall, no cleaner than his room.

"Twenty dollars a month," the lady announced with a demanding smile. "In advance."

Millard paid her and she thumbed the bills carefully. "No cooking in the room," she said and left.

He tested the bed. It was bumpy. He bet it sheltered bedbugs. But he was too tired to care. His eyes kept stinging. He closed them and slept through until the next morning. He awoke still in his clothes.

He walked to Mercy Hospital along the newly named Boulevard of the Allies. The day was overcast and Millard could barely discern the river which flowed below. The smoke which always belched, morning, noon, and night, Sundays and holidays, poured from the chimneys of the J & L Steel Works. He came after an hour to Mercy Hospital, a congery of red brick buildings, lined by leafless privet hedges.

There he found Sister Paulinus in the superintendent's office. She was a tall woman whose mouth and eyes rarely curled or wrinkled with a smile. She bade him sit while she finished filling out the forms before her and then, resting on her elbows, studied him intently, her gray eyes boring into his face.

Millard rubbed his jaw. He wished he had shaved.

"So you'll work for us," she said as though he had accepted an invitation.

"I want to," Millard began. "I have some hospital experience. I could help out with the patients, maybe even work in the pharmacy."

"Father Huber recommended you. I had to scurry, scurry, scurry to find you a place. It's not in the pharmacy and it won't be around the patients."

"Well, I do need a job, any job."

"I am," she continued, unhearing, "perfectly familiar with your situation. As for being a criminal, I am satisfied you have paid your debt to society. I am disturbed about your lobotomy."

"Why?" asked Millard.

"No one should touch God's creation and though you may have been a thief, still it was God's hand which made you. You have changed that handiwork. But there is no point scolding you. It's your doctor that should be punished and I would I could punish him."

Millard licked his lips and asked, "What did Father Huber say about me?"

"He said you were a gentleman, which I can see. He said there might be publicity, which I abhor."

"If there's publicity, Sister Paulinus, it won't come from me."

She stared at him again. At last she broke off and said, "You will work in the housekeeping department. That's what we call our janitorial force. Your supervisor is Sister Ethreda on floor 5 E. You will find her strict but fair. She is our most efficient supervisor. Her floor is the cleanest in the hospital and if you wish to continue here, it will have to stay the cleanest."

"I'll try to keep it clean," Millard promised.

"You work six days a week from 6 A.M. to 2:30 P.M. You are entitled to one meal each day at lunchtime. You will receive one hundred dollars a month. Does that suit you?"

"Thank you," Millard said.

"You will take the elevator to your left and you will find Sister Ethreda on the fifth floor."

Millard edged out of the office and took three deep breaths on the elevator before Sister Ethreda, as stern and starched as her Mother Superior, demanded of him, "Will you keep this ward clean? Keeping this ward clean is God's work and I can't tolerate slovenliness."

"I'll keep it clean," he promised.

Millard was in strange territory. He had never met women who were simply dedicated, not feminine, not anxious to display their tenderness. He had never suspected a woman could bully him but he was fair game for Sister Paulinus and Sister Ethreda.

"I'll show you how I want this done," the nun said, taking his hand. "This is the pail and this is the mop. This is the way I want them used." She showed him. "You have to use this brush for the corners." With that she fell to her knees as gracefully as a ballet dancer and even before she had settled her arm was scrubbing.

"Ready?" she asked him, as positive as a starter's gun.

Millard nodded.

"You do this central hallway, the lavatories, and the nurses' stations. You do not talk to the patients and never to the nurses unless you have to. I'll be back at two-thirty. I expect this floor to shine."

His hands were soft, the pail heavy; he was unaccustomed to constant bending and stooping; the carbolic solution assailed his nostrils and his eyes. But at two-thirty the floor shone. And he thought, gratefully, at least he could work in peace, he was anonymous.

Not for long.

The *Sun-Telegraph* published a story that Monday about the "Brain-burglar," who was working as a cook in Pittsburgh. The reporters professed to have talked to Millard Wright, now out of prison fatigues, clothed in a chef's white hat, promising to "prove to the world and my good friends that my life of crime is gone forever."

The parole officer demanded to know why Millard had granted the interview.

"I work in a hospital," Millard insisted. "I mop floors. I never talked to a reporter."

The tired but dogmatic social worker said, "You're to keep mum, keep yourself out of the papers, unless, of course, you want to go back there for another ten years."

"I don't want to go back," Millard said hollowly. Parole officers were more interested in their paperwork than they ever were in the tamed men who sat across from their desks three times a week at inconvenient hours, humbled and humiliated by their past and present.

"I think I'd *like* to become a chef, though," Millard said. "I'd like to ask Sister Paulinus if I could go into the kitchen."

"You stick to janitorial work," said the officer. "You'll get in less trouble that way. It's honest work. Gives you muscles too. A lot of my parolees are janitors. They're not complaining."

"I'm not either," Millard said. "I'll stay a janitor. But I *would* like to change my room. Three fourteen North Avenue is like living in storage. If I could get a room in the hospital dormitory I'd only have to pay five dollars a month instead of twenty. I could use that money maybe to educate myself."

"Where you live is just fine. We have a hard enough job at this office keeping track of everybody as it is. We'd never get our reports out if we let them all move around at every whim. No, stay where you are."

"Yes, sir," Millard said.

No parole lasts forever, he consoled himself. One day he'd be rid of this man. Unfriendly treatment would not drive him back to crime. Meanwhile he could be stubborn. He began submitting monthly reports:

FINANCIAL REPORT OF MONTHLY EARNINGS

November 1949
Total wages for month including one meal at lunch time (12:00 o'clock) six days a week.

Cash wages received........ $100.00

MONTHLY EXPENSES
1. Dinners for a 30 day calendar month.............. $ 19.50
2. Breakfast for a 30 day calendar month............ 9.00
3. Sunday's lunch—day off—average meal 65¢.......... 2.60

4. Car fare to place of work from North Side......... 6.00
5. Rent for lodging per month........................ 20.00
6. Laundry bill for month........................... 4.00

Total expenses not including
small incidentals........ 61.10

Please note: this does not include the cost of a winter overcoat, galoshes, scarf or hat.

If these interviews with the parole officer humiliated him, so did some of his experiences at the hospital. One of the patients in the ward mentioned to a visiting police officer that the janitor was the famous burglar who had an operation to cure his impulse to steal.

"The whole business was a fake," said the policeman who came daily in mufti. "It was a fraud. And I bet I can prove it."

The policeman planted his gold watch in the lavatory. Setting a lookout to insure Millard was the next man to enter, the patients in the ward assembled behind their door to peep at a man fighting his own primitive desires. Soon enough, Millard pushed open the door and backed in, dragging his pail. More of the patients crowded around the door, waiting.

Ten minutes later, Millard exited, dangling the watch from his hand as though it were contaminated. As he crossed the hall to the ward, the men dispersed, diving into the beds, feigning indifference. The policeman busied his eyes with a magazine. Millard approached, stood over him, letting the watch swing, then gracefully plopped it into the man's lap.

"Once a cop always a cop," he said.

He spent many nights in laborious typing, retelling his autobiography to keep a promise he had made. His eyes burned and strained, but he kept doggedly at it. This time he started with the death of his mother, this time the words were dead weight, without spirit, without buoyancy, without romance. He begged Koskoff to overlook mistakes because he was literally forcing himself. His writing was sparse. He never bothered to identify names and places, he neglected dates. This time he didn't admire anyone. He remembered clearly only the jails and the length of his imprisonments. Throughout he castigated himself and his last chapter was filled with a sense of worthlessness. A melancholy longing pervaded the whole. Even in Koskoff's office, a visit which ordinarily delighted Millard for it gave him the chance to go on at length and inflate his ego, he sat brooding, constantly questioning about his perilous future, wanting to know what justification he had for his meaningless past.

At last good luck. Escaping his forbidding room for a casual walk, Millard saw a cluster of men at the entrance of the Clark Candy Company employment office. He joined them just as they started through the gate. The company put him on as a laborer, stacking the candy boxes in the trucks; cleaning the tubs of chocolate, crystallized sugar, and molasses; freeing the machinery from the gummy substances which dripped and clogged. He was paid thirty dollars a week, turning out Clark Bars and Teaberry Chewing Gum. Sister Ethreda and Sister Paulinus told him he was bettering himself, of course he could leave. Even the parole officer, at Koskoff's urging, let Millard change work.

Yet the man remained depressed. There were biological and psychological reasons for his depressions, and social reasons too. Millard was participating in the American dream, moving onward to chimerical success through effort and work, trying to make more money, trying to win more praise, knowing somehow there is an emptiness to this dream world, that this world has no center of gravity. No one can pride himself on janitorial tasks no matter how well performed, nor is it enough to work in the candy factory. Within the year Millard became a candymaker earning eighty-five dollars a week, skilled now at compounding the artificial sweeteners and flavors, mixing the sugar and molasses and caramel, knowing he still could not take pride in himself until he became a candy distributor, then manufacturer. Perhaps this sense of spiraling dissatisfaction made it all the harder for him to shuck his depression. But society was doing its best for him. Now he had the job and for the first time in his life he also had the girl.

Chapter | 30

The newspaper publicity summoned Roberta Stuckey. One night, when he was only two weeks out of prison, his door, so warped it would never click shut, swung open after a staccato series of soft raps. Millard circled the bed, holding at his chest the book he was reading, and saw, framed in the doorway, a shivering girl, her hair covered by a masculine rain cap, torn brim flapping. He stared at her in confusion, and then with a quick gesture, she ripped the cap off, revealing her auburn hair, shook her head to shed the raindrops, and pleaded, "Millard, don't you remember me? I'm Roberta."

At her feet was a split suitcase, only one strap binding it. In her other hand, she held a shopping bag filled with clothes, a battered portable radio weighing them down.

"You don't remember me at all?" she asked.

"Sure, I remember you," he said.

"You didn't write me."

"I thought about you."

"Aren't you going to ask me in?"

For a few moments there was nothing else to say.

"I don't know about the landlady," he said, going to the door to peer up and down the hall. "She won't let me cook in these rooms."

"I'm not hungry," said Roberta.

"I don't want her to evict me," Millard said nervously.

"She won't let you cook because she doesn't want to clean up. As long as you get a woman out early, I bet I'm all right with her."

"Sit down, sit down," said Millard, gesturing with the book.

Roberta crossed the room to sink in the easy chair.

"What brings you to Pittsburgh?" Millard asked.

"I caught the three o'clock bus from New Kensington," she said. "*You* brought me into town. Don't you know that?"

"I'm just out of stir."

"Why didn't you write?"

His hands brushed away his embarrassment. "So much happened. The operation. Two and a half years." He spread his palms helplessly and finished, "This room."

"It needs new shades." She fingered the stiff, dirty curtain.

He didn't say anything. He moved to the bed. He sank heavily on it. They both heard the ruptured springs squeak.

"Don't you want me?" she asked.

He swallowed, Adam's apple bobbing.

"Is it that hard to say yes or no?" She moved forward on the chair, putting her hand out to clasp the suitcase handle, as though she might sprint from the room with it.

"You came to see me?" he asked hoarsely. "Just me?"

"I need you, Millard."

"Me?" He poked his thumb against his chest. "Me?" he repeated.

"I want someone to take me in, someone who loves me. Someone who won't be just another greedy man, just another night between dirty sheets. I want it to be you, Millard. Aw, please, Millard, it's gotta be you. There's been too many men already."

"Roberta," Millard whispered hoarsely, embracing her, "it's me that needs you. You're saving my life."

She stayed. It cost Millard another ten dollars from his meager salary to make the landlady agree. They had to pretend to her they were married, which she knew was false. Ten dollars was ten dollars.

Their nights were anything but ecstasy. Under the best of

conditions Millard had no sexual confidence and he was recently out of prison and sex-scared. The dirty, shabby room was a strange experience. The woman parading past his bed in her slip was even stranger. For the next weeks he slept in his underwear, his face toward the window, curling up at night like a child in a womb, half-frightened, half-delighted at the presence of the breathing form beside him. She slept in her slip and lingerie, wondering why he didn't want to take them off. But she was in a place, she shared bread and board with a man. It was enough she thought; it would always be enough. Millard was kind to her.

What worried Millard was that his parole officer would hear of the liaison. They were posing as a married couple and without permission to marry, Millard was violating his parole. Yet he did not want to let Roberta go. She wasn't holding him together, but she was holding the remnants of his dream together. Koskoff always insisted on brutal reality; Lou Little regarded him as a waste of time; the parole officer existed just to threaten him. But Roberta, Roberta said she loved him. He wasn't important at work, he wasn't important to others, he doubted now he was important to himself, but he was important to her.

She was unlettered and ignorant. Her speech and her dress betrayed her as the cheap girl from the cheap part of town, her native intelligence no more than it should be. Finding a job was hard work for her. But she trudged the Pittsburgh streets to save the nickel carfare and finally found one as a waitress during the noon-hour rush. She made seven dollars a week plus her tips.

Some nights they ate the cold pimiento cheese sandwiches or the soggy hamburgers she smuggled from the restaurant in her coat pocket. She traced with her finger the scars of the lobotomy, and she traced in her heart those other scars. They talked into the night, night after night. Now when she shivered remembering the cold, he put his arm over her shoulders and whispered to her. They survived together in that cramped room. They even saved money.

With Millard working in the candy factory, the parole officer gave him the permission to move and he and Roberta found three rooms on Monterey Street, not far from work. It was unfurnished but with their little savings, Roberta bought enough pieces from the Salvation Army to make their place a home. They had a bed, this time with a new mattress covered by a chenille spread; new shades with tassel pulls; a veneered bureau; an enamel-top kitchen table with two chairs; and new linoleum.

Once he began to advance in the candy factory, he was able to put Roberta on as one of the cleaning crew. Their joint income was well over one hundred dollars a week, more than sufficient for their needs. That winter Millard bought an overcoat and for Christmas Roberta gave him a woolen scarf. They added two captain's chairs on credit and Roberta for the first time in her life owned her own linens. They even made time payments on a new car, a Chevrolet sedan.

In the end, they had what most people will settle for: appearances. He was almost true respectability, compared to what she'd known. She could follow the forms of fidelity and form satisfied him more than content. She couldn't cook, she never would. She served him hot dogs and Heinz's baked beans, Franco-American spaghetti, Broadcast corned beef hash. She couldn't fry an egg without scorching the white because she never learned to heat the pan slowly. When she served him, however, he felt like the breadwinner at his reward at the end of the day. She was his image of a woman. She was fastidious. She liked to keep things clean, particularly herself. She spent inordinate time arranging and re-arranging her hair. She swept it glamorously up in the morning, and in the afternoon let it down in a maiden's fashion. Up, she behaved like a woman; down, she was an impulsive little girl.

Their respectability united them. Yet the depression remained. Inside of Millard was a frenzy of disappointment. He stayed lonely and moody and silent. She tried to interest him in meeting her friends, in going shopping, in dancing, to no avail. Still he tried but he never got the point. Once in a while he would get up earlier, make breakfast, set the table, and hope to surprise her. One morning she wanted him to join her in bed. She tried to wait him out but he remained at the table.

She called, "Millard, come on back, please, honey."

No response.

Approaching the bed later, he was surprised that she was angry and turned from him.

"If you want to make love so bad you have to shout, why do you turn ice cold?"

"Because it takes you a half hour to hear," she hissed.

"I think you are oversexed," he said, fully believing it.

Innocently, Millard asked his friends at work what a woman likes. One of them said, "They all like a little slap on the fanny." Millard gave her a clumsy slap one night as though he were trying to kill a mosquito and was rewarded, not with a little girl's laugh but with the musical laugh of a mocking woman, a woman resigning herself to the folly of trying to teach a man to experience what he could never feel.

Millard used sex to reduce tensions. He no sooner started than he wanted to finish. The sight of a living woman meant no more to him than the banal smile of a girl on a magazine cover. Roberta tried a transparent sleeping gown, she tried heavy perfume, she tried tender caresses, none of which turned magic. He refused to stir her. He never made her strangely helpless. The sense of touch to Millard was for making sure where things were.

"You know, Millard," she said once, "I used to know a farm-boy. A nice boy. Lived on a farm all his life. He took me there for a picnic and he showed me the chicken house, and the furrows all plowed for planting, and the stable. We sat on a rail fence and in the field all by accident we saw a boar trying to mount a sow. The boar would mount her and she'd just as quick walk away and the boar would snort and chase her. Then he'd mount her and she'd walk away and he'd snort again and go right after her. And we watched this for twenty minutes. It was embarrassing but we couldn't stop watching. I think we were both hoping for the boar. But the sow was so stubborn. Every time he got set, she just walked away and it was like he was falling off a ladder. That boy turned to me and he said, 'Roberta, you know what? Thank God I got hands.' And he put his hands right here! Like this!"

He exhausted her patience. They argued one night. He said he couldn't marry until his parole was lifted. She walked out, the split suitcase bumping against her legs as she tried to slam the door.

The day after that, Millard was admitted to the emergency

room of Montefiore Hospital. He was pale, sallow, cold, and clammy. His pulse was fast and irregular. His blood pressure was low. His breathing was rapid. A blood examination by the resident confirmed profound anemia. He lay in an oxygen tent, a transfusion pouring into his veins, the nurses piling on blankets.

The resident told Koskoff he diagnosed severe upper gastrointestinal bleeding. Millard had a hepatic or duodenal ulcer. "How can a lobotomized man have an ulcer?" the young doctor asked Koskoff.

"It's the somatic price he has to pay for his depression," Koskoff answered.

"Well, he's not the first man to get an ulcer over a woman," the resident said.

Millard's illness aroused Roberta's pity. She came back to him. "You're saving my life again," he told her.

"Will you ever marry me?" she asked.

"I'll marry you," he said. He was as good as his word. In the late summer of 1951, scrubbed and beaming, they came to see Koskoff for the blood test. Maybe this is what the man needs, Koskoff thought, maybe it's what he's always needed.

Koskoff had seen both of them frequently, for he was preparing a monograph on Millard. They came for interviews and he was also able to arrange dental and medical treatments for Roberta. Living with Millard, finding security, if not happiness, made her a more than attractive woman. The fidgeting nervousness and anxiety which lined her face slowly faded; she had put on weight and begun to look more like the curvaceous woman she was instead of a skinny undernourished girl.

"And the day?" Koskoff asked.

"Next weekend, we hope," said Millard. "We always take picnic trips out to the country. The next time around we'll come back Mr. and Mrs."

The couple set out the following Friday evening for Little Washington, an historic city twenty-five miles to the south of Pittsburgh.

"I wish I had an engagement ring for you," Millard said as they passed through suburban Pittsburgh.

Roberta said, "That's all right. It's the ceremony that counts. I always thought I'd be married in a white gown in a pretty church, but this way is fine for me. I don't need mink wraps or new dresses. Being Mrs. Wright is enough."

"You could have all those things—the mink, the rings, new clothes."

"How?" she asked, curious.

"Right over there," he said, nodding his head toward a darkened house. He swerved quickly to the curb and shut off his headlights. "Or from the dark house beside it. No one's home now. They're all away for the weekend. It's always a lead pipe cinch on a hot summer weekend. No one ever takes their mink with them."

"You mean steal?" she asked. "Millard, you'll go back to jail!"

"No, I won't. Not this time. This time I've got a hawk."

"A hawk?"

"You. You're a hawk. A lookout. You see a policeman come down this block, you flick the car lights on and go over and ask him the directions back to Pittsburgh. Then you follow those directions and meet me at home. I'll know, I'll see the headlights blink. Otherwise, wait here till I get back."

"Millard why would you want to steal for me? I don't need those things."

"Not for you. For us. Ten minutes a night and we can have everything we want. The mink, the ring, the nice clothes, money."

"It's too much of a chance," she said, shaking her head. But there was no more disbelief. She knew he meant it. "How can you *think* of taking that chance?"

He turned and touching her face with his hand he said, "The first thing I ever stole was candy from an overturned boxcar. Taking that candy made me feel alive. Now I make candy. I can have all I want. Making candy gives me a bellyache."

Wordlessly she searched his face.

"Now what do I do?" she asked.

The justice of the peace who performed the marriage the next day remembered them. He and his wife thought the Wrights an attractive couple. He even noticed the beautiful ring Roberta wore. He was sure it was an heirloom. He was positive two such well-dressed, courteous people both descended from what he liked to call "family."

Chapter | 31

Never was he better, never more skillful, never more daring. Now there was no clumsiness, now no mistakes. He was more selective in what he stole: only jewels, furs, and money. He never had to hurry. He could search each darkened house more thoroughly because he knew there was a car outside, timed to leave the moment he exited. Roberta was as cool a professional as he was. She never panicked. Only once did she have to warn him. A family returned. Millard had no time to exit. He ducked into the cellar and curled up in one of the slate set tubs, lowering the enamel lid over him. He waited there over two hours before he dared raise the lid and silently slip outside. But there she was: waiting. In fact, she was more than willing to rifle another home that night.

Burglary thrilled her, too, more than he expected it would. A week after their wedding day, when the thrust to rob another home was in him, he said to her, "You'll have to help me. Every time."

"I thought you only wanted the engagement ring and the clothes."

"No. I'm going back to it. I'm nothing without it. You're going to have to help me. Because you helped me once means you're in it, too. You're an accessory before and after."

He never had to use that threat again. She looked forward to the entry and theft as much as he did.

Millard could talk as casually about burglary to Roberta as he could to any cellmate.

"What's the best things to steal, Mil?"

"What we're stealing. Money's the best. Once it's in your pocket it's yours. Then jewels and furs."

"Why don't we try to steal more money then?"

"Because there's not much money in an empty house. We have to hit a house with a wall safe."

"Can you open one of those?"

"I can buy a special jimmy and tear the door right off."

"How can you find one of those houses?"

"I'll show you," said Millard.

On a Saturday thereafter, they would drive out to one of the suburban neighborhoods ringing Pittsburgh and stop at a realty office. Millard again called himself John Livengood and introduced Roberta to the agent as his wife, Mildred. He was moving to Pittsburgh from Scranton to become an executive in one of the steel mills. They wanted to buy a house for thirty or thirty-two thousand dollars. The first time around, he invented an entire family with Roberta's connivance. They had a son in junior high school and two daughters in elementary school. Each of them needed a bedroom and they simply had to have three baths.

Half the time the agent showed them empty houses, but other times they went into homes still inhabited by the owners. Two or three of those had wall safes and Millard and Roberta would watch those homes like birds of prey until they saw the houses deserted.

Other times they put their inspection to immediate use. When Millard began to enthuse about a house, Roberta would know he had spotted something for the taking. As they were leaving, Millard would snap his fingers and say, "If the two desks can fit in that back room, I know this is the house for us. Let me measure." With that, he would pull a tape measure from his pocket and bound back upstairs while Roberta kept the owners and the agent occupied with animated exclamations about the beauty of the view.

In the car he would unclench his fist and show her the brooch or the necklace. He had a professional's eye. When they came into a home, he could accurately gauge over a handshake the worth of a woman's jewelry. If it was expensive jewelry, he knew she had other pins and rings and bracelets equally expensive. He had a supreme ability to guess where she would keep the rest. An experienced postal worker can tell whether there is currency in an envelope or gold in a package. Millard, talking to a home-owner, could tell within minutes the cash value of what that homeowner kept in bureau drawers. Once, on one of these Satur-day expeditions, Millard opened a closet door, with a nail file pried open a locked suitcase, stuck his hand into the suitcase envelope, and slipped a small felt bag of stones from a hiding place its owner thought forever obscure.

These adventures thrilled Roberta. At best she was a waitress, and at that a hash-house waitress. Few people took her seriously. She had been consigned to lowly clerical jobs and she had to live along mean and shabby streets. At last, she was getting back something of her own. When she fluted about the lovely house, when she twisted the ignition as Millard jumped into the car, everything awaited her.

They never made off with a significant stone or necklace, an emerald that could be re-cut or a necklace that could be sepa-rated, but they did steal gold and platinum pieces and they exer-cised great caution in pawning these. Every fourth week, Roberta took the Greyhound bus to Cleveland or Columbus or Cincinnati, and pawned what she could for what price she could get. She told her neighbors she had to visit a sick sister. Nor did they change their ordinary daily patterns. Both of them went to work regu-larly. Millard didn't want a new car with the money; Roberta didn't want new clothes and hats and shoes.

Millard and Roberta were even storing furs. There is always a market for furs. A fur coat is identifiable if it is worn as it was made. But if the fur is unstitched, the coat becomes so many pelts with a value for a furrier. There are lofts in Jersey City and St. Louis whose employees work around the clock unstitching and refinishing furs. These lofts have all the apparatus of a sizable industry—appraisers, drivers, accountants, salesmen, stylemasters. One fur coat isn't worth the risk, but a truckload is. Millard began to collect a truckload.

Their three rooms on Monterey Street couldn't begin to accommodate the number of fur coats he stole. But these rooms were on the top floor of a house beginning its descent from the ultra-respectability of sheltering a family through the generations to the uneasy reputation of opening doors for transients.

The Wrights lived on the top floor. Above them was an insulated attic, a cathedral roof which offered barely enough room for a man to stand upright. The attic had one entry, a trap in the wall. Millard had to stand on the sink to get into it. Nevertheless, he built a vault out of cedar, two racks stretching its distance on which to hang the coats. He cooled the vault with several electric fans he kept whirring all the time. It was makeshift cold storage, but none of the coats shed. He was jamming that vault and he was going to go on forever as every happy man thinks he will go on forever.

He could have.

The police were confused. The stolen goods never appeared in a Pittsburgh pawnshop but the detectives staked out in the bus and railroad terminals—and on the toll bridges—never saw a known burglar. The police had checked every gas station within a forty-mile radius and no night attendant remembered a strange truck or an overloaded car.

But there is always that one cop.

He was Captain William Hanna of the state police. He was a tall, urbane, handsome police officer thoroughly knowledgeable and thoroughly sure.

When the Pittsburgh police officers insisted it was two burglars, Hanna said no, it was one. When these officers pointed out that there were two different methods of operation, Hanna stuck to his guns. But he couldn't put his finger on it. He had seen something in one of the early reports and he couldn't remember what it was but it would show up again and then he would know.

There was something Koskoff's needle had never disturbed. It was Millard's pride. He knew he had skill as a burglar. He was convinced of his intellectual superiority. He might modestly demur to Koskoff's estimation of his intelligence with the apologetic statement, "I'm not as bright as you suppose," but he never demurred to himself. He was always improving his mind. The lobotomy never halted that attempt, never staggered it. But in the end he might just as well have written his name on the doorsill.

"Of course," said William Hanna to himself putting down the report. The home-buyer burglar had stolen an antique gold watch and a sterling silver brush and comb set. He had also stolen, according to the Duquesne professor's deposition, a copy of Abram Kardiner's *Psychological Frontiers of Society* and Sigmund Freud's *New Introductory Lectures on Psychoanalysis.* It *was* one man. Hanna dug out the old reports of stolen property. There is was. The silly son-of-a-bitch had stolen *Psychology* by William McDougall, a dollar book in the old Henry Holt Home University Library series. Who but a lobotomized burglar was interested in psychology?

Chapter | 32

Thus it was that three state policemen from the Butler Barracks arrested Roberta. They came into the apartment, not forcing entry, although they had a warrant; simply brushing by the shocked and frightened woman. She stepped back from the door and the three uniformed men confronted her, demanding where Millard was. Each question was as hard as a blow, and Roberta kept shaking her head to ward them off. The questions were relentless. They succeeded in their aim. They rattled her. She bowed her head and said, "I don't know where my husband is."

"You're married to this man?"

She nodded wordlessly.

"You don't know where he is?"

"Well," she wavered, searching their faces for mercy, "he went to Cleveland yesterday."

"What's he want in Cleveland?"

"I don't know."

"You're married to him."

"I think he went to get some money."

"Where was he going to get it?"

"I don't know."

"You're married to him? You don't know?"

She didn't want to tell them. She never anticipated nor suspected she would have to deal with three heavy-shod policemen, none of whom removed their hats. All of them were more than capable of bullying her. She could contend in her pitiful way with someone who manhandled her. She had learned how to duck and dodge and run. She had no instincts to guide her with authority, booted authority. Soon they were no longer three hardened policemen, they became vengeance and retribution, bound and determined to force her, to make her succumb to her guilt.

"He was going to get the money from the pawnbroker," she finally said.

They began to ransack the apartment, spilling her things from the drawers, moving dressers and couches, flipping back the rug. The story poured from her. Millard would have known to surrender immediately, to hope they would transport him right away to the stationhouse so that somehow some vague chance would let him get rid of the furs and the jewelry and the portable radios and the silverware stored in the attic vault. Not Roberta. She started to cry when she saw they were going to desecrate her home. She told them what she knew they wanted to hear. They stopped. They comforted her. All of it spilled out, dates and houses and pawnbrokers and hiding places.

In that moment, love for Millard fled. Why didn't he tell her? Why didn't she realize it would come to this? Life and marriage and future were thrown in a growing pile of stolen goods there on her living room table.

The policeman crawled into the attic and shouted down in amazement, "My God, will you look what they've got up here!" "They" for it was "they" now, she and Millard, would have all their sins and crimes catalogued. She knew she was going to have to listen to those sins and crimes repeated over and over. She thought of bursting from the apartment, running through the streets, but there was no one to run to, there would be no terminal for her mincing pace. She did start, her body forward in the chair, knuckles stained white as they gripped the arms.

But she held herself back when she heard the policeman in the attic shout to the other two, "For Chrissakes, will one of you watch the prisoner."

They waited for Millard, the four of them, Roberta prone on the bed, her eyes never dry, the sobs choking her, the policemen ignoring her, spending their time in desultory talk. At last, in the late evening, they took her to jail in Butler. He wasn't coming back that night, not Millard. The police had no sooner entered her name on the blotter than the reporters discovered it. Publicity bathed everyone. Hanna sighed. The chances of picking up the returning Millard were gone. His police squadron was mesmerized with its own celebrity as reporters inundated the station.

"You're famous," said a Pittsburgh policeman. "You did everything but catch him."

"I know, I know," said Hanna. "But I ask for men and they send me clowns."

"He's probably halfway to Vegas now."

"No," said Hanna. "He'll be here. I know he'll be here."

"Why? Because you got the woman?"

"No, because we got the goods. That's like stripping him naked."

"I know one thing you got," said the disgruntled policeman, "and that was all the headlines."

The Butler Barracks didn't get *all* the publicity; they shared a large portion of it with Millard. The next afternoon, when he drove back into Pittsburgh, Millard saw the headlines and the photographs of the rich, gleaming, warm things he stole. He read the police had arrested Roberta.

Flight.

He careened through Pittsburgh not knowing where he was bound. Faster and faster he drove, zipping through red lights, not tracking his route by the highway signs, his eyes glazed, following only the white line along the highway. It was as though the panorama flashing by his car windows was the last reel of freedom, now too sweet and poignant a vision to absorb. He knew, despite the sweat which poured from him, the fear which invested his chest and heart and being, that this was his last vision.

He slowed. He knew suddenly where he was. He had driven to a specific place after all. He had arrived in Blairsville. He wheeled his auto through the center of this growing suburban town, realizing he was at last on those familiar streets of which he had dreamed so often.

He drove out to the farmhouse Malcolm Wright had furnished and kept for his family. Where once the hills and the trees had dwarfed the Wright home, now the same house commanded the knoll. Fanning out behind it was a neighborhood development of small homes. Sidewalks curved through what had once been pasture, and the stone walls which outlined Malcolm Wright's little acreage were gone, row upon row of shrubbery shielding hundreds and hundreds of residences. Even the sky was different, filled now with the matrix of imperceptibly swaying telephone wires.

Millard's old homestead was all the area had salvaged from the past. Now the front porch where Malcolm rocked on summer evenings was screened; patio furniture with gaudy plastic prints occupied all the space. The tree to which Millard's father had once affixed a swing was gigantic and bushy with leaves. New shutters in bright blue framed each of the windows.

Millard parked and waited and studied. A young boy turning square corners mowed the lawn with an orange Reo rotary. A car crunched to a stop in the stone driveway. A suburban matron and her daughter wrestled the bags of groceries from the rear of a stationwagon into the kitchen door.

If he waited, if he spent the time until dark in idle cruising, he knew he could burglarize that home. But why? he thought. These would be the last things he'd ever steal. The game was up and he knew it. Roberta was gone. Not her fault, he knew, but he was alone again, the dream once and for all dust. He had disgraced Roberta, disgraced them all, the few friends he had collected whose love he had wanted but never deserved. He simply was too weary to go on. Even if he could, where would the journey take him? There was no place left to go. Better let someone else determine his course. He drove to the Butler Barracks.

An aching sadness made it impossible for him to hear all the questions Captain Hanna asked. Groggily Millard said, "All I want to do tonight is turn myself in. I want to see my wife. That's all. I'll tell you everything else in the morning."

"All right," said Captain Hanna, "bring his wife in. But I can't give you much time with her. You'll have to make it quick. Let the reporters have a picture, please. I don't want them stamping through the jail all night."

They did not embrace when a police matron led Roberta into the room. She stared at him tearfully and sat at the table, wearily suffering through the blinding flash bulbs of the eager photographers. She waited with her hands in her lap, not looking at him. Millard stared straight ahead.

"What happens to us?" she asked.

"We'll have to tell them what we did."

"Will they put me in jail?" she asked, hoping against hope he would offer to protect her.

He nodded.

"I don't want that to happen to me," she sobbed. "Why does it have to happen to me?"

"Because nothing worked out for us. The operation didn't work out, the judge didn't work out, the job didn't work out, nothing worked out."

"I guess love didn't work out, either." At last she touched him.

"I guess we didn't let it," he offered. "I guess we just didn't." They were the hardest words he'd ever uttered.

Her lips quivering, her hands in agitated movement, she left the room. She didn't look pretty anymore. She was wearing the faded dress she had on when the state police came. Her shoes, low oxfords, were old. They were loose and flapped against her heels. She had tried to sweep her hair up, but she lacked a mirror in the cell. It was a clumsy arrangement.

"Want anything?" asked Captain Hanna.

"A glass of milk," said Millard, his throat dry.

They led him, weak and helpless, to a cell. They took away his belt and his shoelaces. They always did that to keep a man from suicide. Let them.

The iron pipes, the steel bars, the soiled and dirty canvas cot stretched between two chains always signaled what will happen in the morning. In the morning, Millard knew, you will tell them. They will keep at you until you tell them every last robbery, every last item. You have to be brave with them like you are with a dentist. The pipes, the bars, the porcelain commode, the bare, darkened concrete walks rob a man of bravado, of anger, of jealousy, of impulse; they rob a man of everything except regret. Millard regretted that he could never amount to anything except in here.

"What are you in for?" asked a man in an adjacent cell.

"I'm bagged for burglary."

"I shot someone," said the man. "I shot her husband. He broke in the door and tried to kill me. I've got twelve stitches over my eye. He's the criminal. And they lock me up."

"Where'd you get the gun?" asked Millard.

"I'm an auxiliary fireman. I had a permit. I was defending myself. He's a sadist and they lock me up. How d'ya like that?"

"If her place wasn't on fire," Millard said, "you got a lot of explaining to do."

"Go to hell," said the man. "What are you? Some kind of lawyer or something."

"I used to be a jailhouse lawyer," said Millard wearily.

The man had retired to his cot. Millard peered through the confining bars and saw the man's slouched shoulders, head buried in his hands.

That was the sum of what Millard was—he knew everything about jail. He was his most efficient in jail. If these state policemen thought they could stump him, he resolved, they had another think coming.

"Guard," Millard called, "can you do me two favors? I'd like a pencil and some paper and I'd like you, please, to open that window. It's awfully hot in here."

"Sure," said the guard. He climbed atop Millard's cot and unlocked the small wired window. Behind the wired glass were bars.

"All I could find is this white cardboard," he said to Millard. "That and a pencil will have to do. The office is locked up."

"Thank you very much," said Millard. "That will do fine."

He watched the guard disappear down the concrete alley. The trigger-happy lover next door had fallen asleep.

Now Millard was the only man awake in the small cell block.

He wrote three suicide notes, tearing off sections of the card-board as he finished each. He made them short, hurrying before the immense weariness returned, knowing if it returned he would fail. He took off his eyeglasses, and holding them flat in his palm, smashed them against the curve of the commode. Unable to see, he knelt on the floor, and gently testing with his hand, picked up every splinter. He selected the longest one and dumped the rest into the bowl. Quickly, coolly, he sliced through the vein in his left wrist. With his left hand already bleeding profusely, he sliced the vein on his right wrist. He dropped the last splinter into the commode and flushed them all down into the waste-line. He investigated the bowl. None left. Again he felt the floor. None there.

Then he dropped the empty eyeglass frames through the window, and ripped off his T-shirt. He tore it and tied a knot around one of the bars in the window. He lay flat on his cot, stretched the T-shirt into a noose around his neck and moved to the very edge.

He could feel the blood pumping from his wrists and hear the drops splattering against the floor. The weariness returned, enveloping him. He would be weak soon and he would tumble from the cot and hang himself.

Chapter | 33

For the summer of 1952, David Koskoff had rented a bungalow at the foot of the Alleghenies. It had no electricity, no running water, no telephone. He and his family were miles from the nearest store and the nearest neighbor was over the mountain. The Koskoffs had been there four days when at dawn a young boy throwing good-size pebbles against the window awakened them shouting, "Dr. Koskoff! Dr. Koskoff!"

"The hospital has found me," Koskoff groaned. It had to be the hospital. They were the only ones who knew where he was. But it wasn't the hospital.

"The state police want to talk to you on the phone. We have to go to my house," the boy said. "My mother said to get you."

The boy and Koskoff drove recklessly over the mountain, descending to the farm on the far slope. The doctor hurried through the screen door and his grim-faced neighbor, whom he had never met, ominously gave him the number of the state police.

"Captain William Hanna," the voice on the other end said.

"I'm Dr. David Koskoff."

"The neurosurgeon?"

"Yes."

"Dr. Koskoff, I thought you'd like to know Millard Wright committed suicide here in jail last night."

"Suicide?" asked Koskoff. "Why?"

"He turned himself in. He was wanted for burglary. Didn't you see the papers?"

"No, Captain, I didn't. Does his wife know?"

"She's here under arrest. Yes, she knows."

"Is she all right?"

"No," said Hanna, "she's in pretty bad shock. We think our doctor is bringing her out of it."

"Did you want me to help?" asked Koskoff.

"Not exactly. I remembered you performed a lobotomy on Wright several years ago and I thought you might want to make an autopsy."

"I'll be right over," said Koskoff. Within him was a tumult, a tumult composed of shock, sadness, and anger. The shock was over the suddenness, the sadness from a sense of mutual defeat he and Millard now shared, and the anger was at those who said the experiment wouldn't work who now were right. Koskoff felt such urgency to find out what had happened that he left the farm and drove immediately to Butler. It wasn't until he reached the Barracks that he realized here he was, a harried, unshaved man in a T-shirt, wearing loafers which didn't match.

William Hanna told him about Roberta's arrest and how Wright had appeared at the desk the night before.

"How many robberies had he committed?" Koskoff asked.

"Roughly twenty-eight. There's probably another dozen or so but he didn't get the chance to tell us about them. You didn't know he was robbing homes?"

Wordlessly Koskoff shook his head.

"No idea at all?" the Captain asked.

"It was the one question I never asked," Koskoff said. "I suppose I was afraid of the answer. When he stopped discussing an honest life, I should have known, shouldn't I?"

"You had every reason for not wanting to know but you should have known."

"Exactly what did he say?"

"Doctor, he was in terrible despair. I could *feel* it, a profound humiliation at what he had done to himself. No, he was quiet, resigned, I'd say. And the wife was too confused, too frightened, to make much sense."

"This conviction would have been the end of the road for him."

"This would have been the lifetime stretch, no question about that, Doctor. But from the way he acted, I'd guess he was much more remorseful about what he'd done to himself than what the State of Pennsylvania was going to do to him."

"I wish he'd known that I would have forgiven him. How did he manage the suicide?"

"It's my fault really," the Captain said. "Just like not knowing was yours. We both should have guessed. Ordinarily, in a case like this, we'd interrogate the prisoner. But I figured Wright had had a tough enough day. He knew what he was in for, what was waiting. I was going to question him when he pulled himself together. I told the other officers to go easy on him. If he needed anything within reason, give it to him. We knew from his dossier he had always been a good prisoner, never acting up, never trying escape."

"He showed no sign of suicide?"

"All he asked for was a glass of milk. Around eleven he asked Officer Barger to open the window of his cell. It was a hot night. Barger did and Wright asked him could he have pencil and paper. Reasonable enough, right? You wouldn't figure him for a suicide."

"In this instance, perhaps not. But he was suicidal. And he was devious."

"This was real mischief," the Captain went on. "He wrote three notes, and then he took his eyeglasses and broke them against the commode."

"He couldn't see without his glasses," Koskoff said.

"With one of the slivers," Captain Hanna went on, "he cut the main artery in each wrist. You know what he did then?"

Koskoff leaned forward.

"He flushed all the glass down the commode. Picked it all up. If Officer Barger hadn't remembered his eyeglasses, we'd still be searching that cell for the weapon."

"You couldn't bring him back?"

"He made sure of that, too. He made a noose out of his shirt and tied it to the bars outside the opened window. When he passed out from loss of blood and collapsed, he hanged himself. Officer Katsur found him sometime after midnight. These are the notes he left."

The Captain handed Koskoff the three pieces of cardboard. The first read:

Officer Barger . . . Thank you and all the other officers for everything. You've been very kind.

and the second:

Dr. Koskoff, Rev. Swoyer [Roberta's minister], Bill Heagy, Chaplain Stremel and Father Huber, and those I harmed,
please forgive me.
I die in sincere sorrow.

To Roberta he wrote:

Goodbye, my darling:
Give my eternal love to my good, loyal wife who has been more to me than I deserve. I am sentencing myself to death for my evil misdeeds.

Millard

Koskoff rose and said to the Captain, "You've been more than kind. If Roberta will give me permission, I will certainly want an autopsy."

"We have her over in the women's wing. Maybe she'd like to talk to you."

"What will happen to her?" Koskoff asked.

Captain Hanna shrugged. "She was his accomplice. I can't see how she can possibly avoid pulling a five-to-ten-year rap."

In the other wing, Koskoff came upon Roberta, small and helpless in a large wooden chair. Her eyes were sunken and when she saw him, the blood rushed from her face. She flinched when he came near her, as though she expected him to strike.

"Roberta," Koskoff said gently, "I'm sorry for Millard and sorrier for you."

She toyed with her handkerchief and the last of her composure fled. She kept twisting the linen around her fingers. Her mouth twitched. She blinked rapidly.

"Why couldn't you tell me, Roberta?" he went on. "We might not have spared him but we could have spared you. Why couldn't you tell me?"

"I was afraid," she said, her voice grainy and hoarse.

"Of me?" asked the doctor.

"Of him," and she pointed through the window to the cells which lined the other side of the green lawn.

"Millard?"

She nodded.

"What were you afraid of?"

"He told me I could never leave him because I helped him. He said he would do terrible things to me."

"Millard made those threats?" Koskoff asked, incredulous.

"Oh no, no. I didn't tell you because I loved him. That's why. Because I loved him. I'm the only one who really loved him. That's why I didn't tell."

"A lot of us tried to help," said Koskoff.

"But helping people," she said between sobs, "is *helping* them, not just sometimes, all the time. You have to help people for them, not for yourself. Mr. Little just got him into the newspapers. You just cut open his head. I tried to teach him how to make love. He didn't know how to do that. He was a grown man and nobody had ever cared enough to tell him how. You'd think somebody sometime would have started there." The handkerchief at her eyes could not dam the cascade of tears.

By the next day the newspapers were filled with the story.

A habitual burglar who underwent a rare brain operation to cure an uncontrollable urge to steal only to resume his life of crime five years later, imposed his own final sentence today—death by suicide.
"A lobotomy reduces self-control," said Dr. Edward Mayer. "Therefore, an operation of that kind cannot be, in my estimation, conceived as one to give the individual better control over his impulses." (*The New York Times*)

Millard F. Wright, burglar and social enigma, will be buried tomorrow afternoon, leaving behind this medical puzzle:
Was the operation on his brain in 1947 a success or failure?
The answer is hidden behind the curtain of silence traditionally main-

tained by the medical profession when laymen become too curious. (*Pittsburgh Post Gazette*)

And in the same paper Lou Little said:

I am really disillusioned. Wright visited me often and was in my office not long ago. He was doing fine, I thought. He told me both he and his wife were working and making money and that they planned to buy a home. He said he never thinks of stealing.

At Butler Hospital the next morning, Koskoff met Dr. Ralph Weaver, the coroner.

"Would you like to assist me?" Weaver asked.

"Yes, I would," answered Koskoff.

"Then," said Weaver, "I'll perform the autopsy and let you remove the brain. Maybe some good will come of it. I hope so. He certainly put a lot of people to trial and error with no benefit yet. Let's hope he has something for us after all."

They uncovered Millard, stiff and gray; like most of the dead, looking unlike himself. Whatever the unhappiness that surrounded his existence, that drilled and re-drilled him, the ambience was gone, evaporated. This stiff flesh, these locked eyes, and so many entries in so many dusty ledgers were all that remained.

Koskoff removed the brain. It was unmarred. Millard Wright's legacy to science, such as it was, was in excellent condition. There were no terminal effects of anoxia, such as edema, thrombosis, or hemorrhage. Because he had virtually bled to death, his brain was exsanguinated and Koskoff could see immediately that except where he had performed the bilateral lobotomy the surface disclosed only normal configurations. Koskoff had cut precisely where he intended. There were no surprises.

But Dr. Weaver had one. "Look at that," he said to Koskoff. He pointed with his scalpel to the exposed inner surface of the stomach.

"Cancer," said Koskoff. "Why, the man had cancer of the stomach."

"He didn't have six months," said Weaver. "All he had to do was wait."

"It would have been painful," said Koskoff, examining the deteriorated tissues.

"Well, he would at least have been spared the suicide," said Weaver.

"That was never Millard Wright's way," said Koskoff. "The grave public wrong was his way."

Outside the operating room, Koskoff tried to brush by the ring of reporters who surrounded him. He told them Wright would have died of cancer of the stomach.

"Come on, Doc, one statement. That's not violating the Hippocratic oath."

"Millard Wright's suicide," he began, "is a measure of his capacity to feel, to hate, perhaps to love. Certainly to suffer. As his physician, I feel the sense of personal loss every physician feels when a patient entrusted to his care for a long time dies."

On July 1, 1952, five years to the day after Judge McDonald sentenced him, Millard's funeral services were held in the Sirlin Home on the North Side of Pittsburgh, not far from Monterey Street. Reverend Swoyer told the small assembly of friends how for a brief time during the forty-two years of his strange and bizarre life, Millard had carried some of the hopes of the medical and scientific worlds, that he probably struggled to fulfill promises made in good faith; but those promises were too much for him to bear.

Roberta Stuckey Wright, a police matron beside her, walked toward the bier, faltered momentarily, then bent and kissed his lips.

He was cremated that afternoon. Millard Wright was at last splendid, Koskoff thought, as Thomas Browne's verse came to him: "Man is a noble animal, splendid in ashes and pompous in the grave."

Epilogue

Koskoff entrusted Millard Wright's brain to Dr. Paul Yakovlev of Harvard, a renowned neuropathologist, neurologist, and philosopher. The prospect of this evaluation was so important to Yakovlev that within hours of Koskoff's request, he flew from Boston to Pittsburgh.

Yakovlev made a complete study. By August he was able to write Koskoff that Millard's contribution could not fail to become one of the capital works in surgical psychiatry.

In November of 1952, Koskoff presented "The Case of Millard Wright" to a congress of neurosurgeons, psychiatrists, neurologists, and other scientists in Madrid at the centenary celebration of the birth of Santiago Ramón y Cajal, the pioneer of modern neurohistology.

Koskoff described Yakovlev's study to the congress. It explained much about the brain's correlation between space, time, and value. Space, of course, was the organism itself; time, the decisions it was able to make; value, the behavior it had dictated. The architecture of Millard's brain was in excellent condition. The lobotomy had been precise and modest. It did exactly what it set out to do and no more. It affected only the frontal lobes. There was no metastatic pathology; the stomach cancer had in no way affected this specimen. In short, Millard Wright had offered the best example of a lobotomized brain Yakovlev had ever examined.

As he finished his report, it occurred to Koskoff how Millard would have reveled in this meeting—the big shot at last. But the assembly greeted Koskoff's comments with silence. Their silence shouldn't have surprised Koskoff. These men, after all, were much more concerned with controlled animal experimentation. They wanted clinical findings which could be reproduced over and over again in laboratories all over the world. Their silence shouldn't have surprised or disappointed Koskoff, but it did. Millard Wright was still eccentric.

After Koskoff had pushed his notes into his briefcase and taken his seat, Almeida Lima, Moniz's colleague, one of two men who had accomplished the first successful lobotomy fifteen years before, pushed in beside him. Lima was a little man who resembled the comedian Cantinflas. In his husky voice, in flawless English, he asked more and more about the experiment. When it came time for the two surgeons to part later that afternoon, Lima paused before his good-bye and said, "You have undertaken a great task. Be sure to finish it." And before leaving for Madrid, Dr. Henry W. Brosin, Professor and Chairman of the Department of Psychiatry at the University of Pittsburgh, told Koskoff, "A doctor if he is lucky will perform this operation under these circumstances only once in his lifetime. The emotional investment is too much. You were changing Millard, but he was also changing you."

Over the next few years the little history Millard Wright had constructed came apart fragment by fragment. Roberta Stuckey Wright tried to convince a jury she had been an accomplice under duress. The plea failed and she served two years in a women's prison, finally winning a Christmas amnesty. Afterward she disappeared into the Southwest but every December Koskoff received a Christmas card from her.

Lou Little went on to greater influence at the bar and in politics. He became a rich man. He was always surrounded by a coterie, never alone. Yet when he suffered the first of his heart attacks, these friends somehow lost interest. Gradually they dropped off and on the night his last heart attack killed him, Lou was all alone, he who loved the company of others so much, his flair for personal publicity exhausted.

So it took Doctor Yale David Koskoff a long time before he could write a tentative finis to what Millard Wright had meant. That finis came on a December day many years later. Pittsburgh had just had its first snowfall of the winter, four inches, just enough to impede traffic and delay Dr. Justin Gallagher, driving in from McKeesport. Dr. Gallagher had referred a patient to Koskoff for a lobotomy, an operation performed the preceding Tuesday.

The patient was a thirty-seven-year-old mother in the terminal stage of an excruciating cancer. This patient knew the cancer was terminal and as her pain increased her anxiety and depression deepened. Her family could no longer care for her. To relieve this anxiety, to return this woman to her family for at least a few months, Drs. Gallagher and Koskoff had determined on a lobotomy. The operation banished the depression. She was no longer concerned with numbering her last days.

That Friday, when the two doctors met at the hospital, Koskoff told Gallagher the operation had succeeded. The patient could return home. "You'll want to see for yourself," Koskoff said. "I had two interns assist me because lobotomies are rarely performed these days and I wanted them to see one."

"You know," said one young intern to both Koskoff and Gallagher, "I heard that someone at Montefiore lobotomized a kleptomaniac about two or three years ago."

From Gallagher a big grin.

"It wasn't a kleptomaniac," Koskoff said. "It was a burglar. And it wasn't two or three years ago, it was nineteen."

"I knew it was something like that," said the young doctor.

As Gallagher and Koskoff walked down the corridor to the elevator, Gallagher commented, "You didn't correct him about the lobotomy."

"I would only have embarrassed him. But you can see now, I'm not fashioning stories when I tell people this operation on Millard Wright still has repercussions. It's still gossip."

"Tell me, Koskoff," said Gallagher, "what did you learn from

that lobotomy—what more than Harlow learned from the crowbar case over one hundred years ago?"

"Harlow didn't get to study Gage before the injury. I learned
a great deal more about Wright than he learned about Gage.
Also, Harlow wasn't as lucky as I. He did not have Paul Yakovlev
to verify the exact site and extent of the damage to Wright's
brain. The rest of Wright's brain was not changed. But the lesions
I introduced still caused behavioral changes and disturbances.
They were complex changes in awareness, feelings, words,
thoughts. We learned a lobotomized man can commit suicide. In
other words, he can still suffer."

"You learned," said Gallagher, "that Millard Wright could go
back to his old ways."

Koskoff stopped him. "No. More. In an age when medicine is
beginning to attempt human experimentation, heart transplants
and the like, we learned restitutive processes may be partly psychological."

They stepped into the elevator.

"Which means . . . ?" asked Gallagher.

"No matter how advanced are our techniques, when we deal
with human beings we have to expect the unknowns and the
imponderables."

Appendixes

In Search of Decisive Judgments[*]

In quest of a critical experiment in behavior the observer can expect no more than the opportunity to study a living man before and after the placing of a specific lesion in his brain and to be able to verify the site and extent of that lesion on postmortem examination. This was the opportunity in the case of Millard Wright.

Certain decisive judgments may be made in the framework of a limited experimental design and in terms acceptable to the traditional scientist. For example, it is important to know that bilateral frontal lobe lesions unaccompanied by neuropathological changes in other parts of the brain produced significant behavioral disturbances of varying levels of complexity including alteration in awareness, affect, words, and thought.

Gradually and at varying rates these disturbances in behavior subsided. How did this come about? Postmortem examination discloses scar tissue at the site of surgery. This is the way tissue heals. In the brain there are no new neural anatomical pathways to take the place of the injured ones for transmission purposes. One can postulate that healthy brain tissue adjusts to the injured structures to restore intrinsic neural balances in systems within the brain or that other transmission systems "vicariously" take over the function of the injured part. This presupposes "localization" of behavioral patterns of differing degrees of

* From an unpublished Case Study by Yale David Koskoff, M.D.

complexity from somnolence to thought. For this there is no evidence. One may say that the widespread disturbances following the modest injuries in the frontal lobes of Millard Wright were healed by restitutive psychological processes.

In terms of experimental procedure it is in the dynamic phase of recovery from injury that decisive observations are to be made. Recovery of the downgraded organism to its pre-injury level unfolds facets of the ontological maturation of the mind of the individual. It is only in this kind of study that one can be sure what the pre-injury capacities were since studies of brain damage which depend on accidental injury or disease can only infer the pre-trauma status of the man. In the case of this man the word proved to be the best guide to the evolution of thought following its "dissolution." It is the word which is the bridge from processes in the mind to conscious operations involved in the perception of reality.

Let us now turn to the reduction in affect or feeling observed for a varying period following lobotomy. If we accept the premise there is no pure affect, that is, feeling without an associated idea, then it becomes obvious that when the volume of ideas is reduced as it is in post-lobotomized patients, feeling must be diminished, in all probability proportionate to the degree of loss of capacity for thought. Thus, this commonly noted effect of lobotomy does not require a patho-anatomic explanation, namely, that certain brain centers mediating emotion or feeling are involved, any more that it requires invoking disturbances of "speech centers" to understand the language disorders noted. Paucity of ideas may also underlie the lack of motivation, restriction in the ability to plan and diminution in dreaming observed in some post-lobotomy patients.

The problem of anxiety as it relates to frontal lobotomy is, I believe, of special significance. Our studies failed to reveal a diminution in anxiety following surgery. On the contrary, the document analysis showed more "distress" after the lobotomy than before. It is pertinent to ask what kind of anxiety is a patient experiencing? That is, from what sources is it derived?

Lobotomy may cut down concern by the mechanism described above. But, in some patients the awareness of the damage to the self elicits greater anxiety detected for the most part by the defenses used to guard against its revelation to the self and others. And because these defenses are often attractive and sometimes even humorous they go unrecognized by the observer, who sees in them signs of improvement over the overt manifestations of suffering noted preoperatively. What it adds up to is this. In the last analysis, assuming the brain lesions are not overwhelming, factors intrinsic in the personality play the decisive role: the strength of the self, the importance to the self of the "proud superstructure" of mind, the time in the life situation when the injury occurred, in short the adaptive capacity of the whole human being.

So far our judgments have been derived from observations in the organism. What can be decisively stated about the man who underwent this lobotomy and what happened to him? And more significantly, perhaps, how does what happened to this man apply to others?

How to study *a* man and make such study significant for Man? A man has limitless parameters ever shifting in kaleidoscopic configurations. The parameters vary in terms of how he regards himself in life situations lived and being lived. Medical psychology has in the last fifty years, largely through the impetus and revelations of psychoanalysis, given us ways of looking at the behavior of an individual and has offered explanations concerning reasons for the behavior. In the psychological defenses used to reconcile the needs of the self and the demands and regulations of others one can learn most about the nature and strength of the instinctual life, the psychosexual developments and the nature of the self in relation to others.

In the case of Millard Wright we may make decisive judgments that he used neurotic defenses particularly involving visual anxieties, that psychosomatic adaptations utilized the gastro-intestinal tract as a "target organ." We learned of the utilization of compulsive mechanisms for the resolution of tensions with manipulative and controlling components. Turning from specific defenses with known origins in early life to more general considerations of the contemporary man we found elements of hope and despair, a kind of prideful self-importance side by side with full knowledge that he was a "fake" and "impostor."

What can one say decisively about the reasons for his acting out against others? Whitehead points out that attack on the environment is the most prominent fact in a man's existence. The reason for the attack is threefold: to live, to live well, to live better. Millard wanted to live but death beckoned seductively. The active attack against the environment was in Millard's case self-punitive yet afforded him social identity. Despite his protestations of anger about society there was a histrionic quality about his acting out even to professed though unrealized Robin Hood characterizations. It was in these dramatics that he gave himself a viability he could not manage because of his despair.

One would gather that with the above insights it would not be difficult for the medical psychologist to decide with assurance the diagnostic category which best fits this kind of person. Was Millard Wright the "normal" man I had initially sought as a "control" case? He was certainly not "anxiety-free" as a normal man is usually conceived, nor did he consistently perceive reality with definitive accuracy and make appropriate judgments, nor was he capable of mature love or self-rewarding work. But do these deficits make him necessarily abnormal? Many useful and sometimes very great people do not meet some or all of the criteria mentioned. He did exhibit attempts at growth as a person, a sincere desire to educate himself and a need for self-expression. He was not without insight.

I believe many diagnosticians would be comfortable with designations such as "psychopathic personality," "sociopath," "character disorder." It is true that Millard Wright acted out against society, that he was impulsive and on brief examination appeared to have shallow feelings. The designations do not encompass the struggles within the self, they miss the hope, they sidestep the despair, they make the person distant from much that is human and with which the observer may identify. Certain diagnosticians would describe aspects of Millard Wright's behavior as schizoid in emphasizing his apparent confusion of identity, poor affect quality and the nonviable nature of many personal inter-relationships, disregarding Millard Wright's essentially appropriate use of words and elements of creativity and accurate self-appraisal. Others would talk of depression as a manifestation of affective psychosis, thus categorizing a man in terms of a mood.

It appears to me that diagnostic classification is of no particular value in this kind of a study where one is attempting to assess what a man is like before the introduction of a procedure designed to change his way of regarding himself and his world. Such classification is misleading, constricting and lends itself to statistical appraisal.

It may be decisively stated that following the frontal lobotomy Millard Wright remained a pain-complaining person who worried about his eyes. He continued to have gastro-intestinal disturbances with painful abdominal symptoms before and during his gastro-intestinal hemorrhages. It is significant that in this instance lobotomy was performed before the onset of the ulcer-cancer syndrome, thus furnishing an unexpected opportunity to test the effect of frontal lobotomy as a prophylaxis against the development of anxiety associated with pain which so clearly constitutes suffering. Tension and anxiety were unrelieved by the surgery. In about one month the style of language characteristic of Millard Wright before lobotomy had completely returned.

And while it is true that for a time at least Wright experienced fewer dreams following lobotomy he did "day dream" and experienced sustained anger on occasion. It is obviously not true of the post-leucotomized Millard Wright that he avoided adventure and sought a more or less stereotyped routine of activities.

Dramatically illustrative of the way he dealt with himself in the continuing failure to adapt to internally derived problems is the ultimate destruction of the self. It is a paradox in the study of a man that the most crucial data, namely the nature of his interaction with others is so difficult to assess. This is so not only because of the uniqueness of a man but also because of the varieties of people he interacts with in varying circumstance and time. Decisive judgments in regard to interpersonal relationships remain elusive.

In the case of Millard Wright there was the advantage of observing him in action, of knowing at least in some degree the significant people with whom he interacted and to have the opportunity to participate in major encounters involving the man in his environment. The observations were made after the frontal lobotomy but validated to a great extent the concept of the man gained pre-operatively through verbal documentation.

Insofar as Millard Wright's patterns of function in his situation are concerned, the hard core of our data rests upon the unassailable fact that his pattern of operation as a thief was essentially unchanged by bilateral frontal lobotomy. These observations are ample evidence of the patient's return of capacity to plan, considered injured in patients with frontal lobotomy.

The nature of Millard Wright's interpersonal relationships remained arrestingly intact following lobotomy; relationships with his lawyer, with the church, the police, his doctor, his wife. He remained detached, manipulative, planning, conniving and at times effective, performing in the style befitting his self-concept and others in the seen and unseen audience. Wright was actor and director in life's scenes with minimum affective cost. He was bemused, chuckling, and at times wrathful. He was a man of style, with faithfulness to his own technique. Prophecy of self-destruction clearly stated in his first communication was neatly fulfilled. Suicide, considered a rare occurrence following frontal lobotomy, demonstrated again the indestructible nature of his behavior pattern.

Outline of the dynamics of aggression (see diagram) toward the self out of the well of despair can only be an educated diagram of vectors but can carry no true notion of the innumerable transactions

218 | THE DARK SIDE OF THE HOUSE

from infancy to death, each burdened with the residue of previous experiences, for the most part abortive and unrealized; a struggle for adequacy culminating in nonachievement. There was failure of all defenses in warding off the destructive force of instinctual aggression in the service of depression. Each defense, the oral with its appetite for food and speech and the anal with its compulsive, controlling and sadistic derivatives, the neurotic somatization of eyes and gut, and finally the neurotic acting out offered a little of Millard in strategic retreat before the onslaught. With all other defenses breached, heightened self-importance, augmented by the incorporation of the positive image of the lost loved one and magnified to fill the void of nonachievement of mature love, was not sufficient to check the relentless attack of instinctual aggression against the self. Need for punishment was deeply rooted in the man. For Millard Wright the lobotomy itself was simply a part suicide in the drift toward death. Only the role of the redeemer of the guilt of all was the part he could play in the societal drama.

DIAGRAMMATIC REPRESENTATION OF THE DYNAMIC FACTORS IN THE SUICIDE OF MILLARD WRIGHT

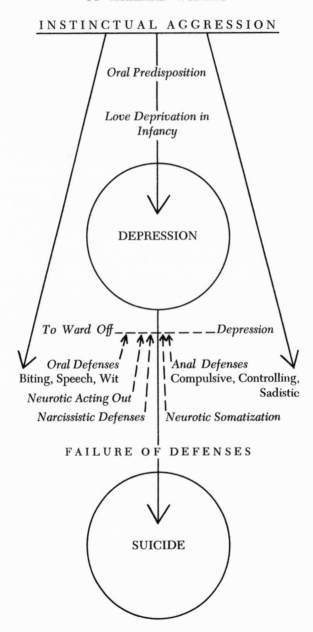

FACSIMILES OF PRE-OPERATIVE AND
POST-OPERATIVE WRITINGS
BY MILLARD WRIGHT

Millard Wright's pre-operative handwriting.

10-20-47

Dear Dr. Kosboff:

The phase of my case-history which I excluded from everyone was that I had developed a propensity to rob the wealthy or might I add further the middle class folk. This bias grew out of an intense hatred brought on by maltreatment from the age of 4 to 17. It seems, when viewing this matter in careful retrospect, that those who reared me such as my school teacher, father, and not to forget the harsh, severe treatment I received at the hands of the police at the age of 14. I was sent to a reform school for a mere nothing and charged with incorrigibility. From then on it was one place after another. I began hating "authority" and what it represented. Thus my crime career can truly be based on an insane impulse to get revenge against society. To me the police and what they stood for represented society. After a few years of deliberate stealing, I got a kick out of burglarizing the wealthy + middle class folk's homes. Even though I didn't need the stuff I stole, I still took it always getting a feeling of elation and self-satisfaction of getting revenge against those who I felt had it coming to them for their bad treatment of me in my youth.

I was afraid to give this information at the Montefiore to you, in addition to this I had not carefully analyzed my past actions. However, after precise and thoughtful analysis of the past, I arrived at the foregoing conclusion. This could be fallacious reasoning on my part, yet I honestly believe it is basically true in substance. What I write here is only the outline of the aspect.; I should like to discuss the matter at greater length sometime when you have time.

note: The hostility which the prosecution displayed at various moments, caused me to be cautious in what I said, for I knew that all that it could yet which would be adverse to my case, would be employed against me. after I left your care, everything I wrote and said was carefully scrutinized for weak points. I was doubly cautious.

One day I should like to do some writing. But nothing will be written for publication till it meets your approval and Dr. Besides, it's too premature to say anything. I haven't pro. myself, yet.

Respectfully,

Minora

P.S.
Don't forget the typewriter search.

A pre-operative letter addressed to Dr. Koskoff.

Upon leaving prison in 1944, I was below par. To give you an example of what condition I was in. About sixth days after I was out, I was courting a neighbor girl. She was somewhat of an athlete and a lovely girl, physically and mentally. One Sunday we were out walking in the woods. Well, to make the story short, she wanted a little loving but I was unable to please her. So when a man is unable to give some satisfaction he must be low in vitality. I realized this and ate the best food I could get. In six months I came around gradually and was able to have a little pleasure. The first six months upon parole, my eyes gave me great trouble, I mean eye aches at least three times weekly and they were severe too. However, I'll drop this angle at the present.

When I left prison I was resolved to save money at all costs. At the time I was arrested I had accumulated one thousand dollars. I met the girl from Indiana and we had a pleasant courship for many months. In my opinion she had a Cinderella complex. She was still living in her girlhood. Of all the months I went with her she wouldn't let me spend a nickle on her. I hate to say this but the girl footed all the bills and would show anger when I insisted on paying, so I got in the habit of letting her pay the bills. I had visited her in July 1945 and had arranged to marry her after I had secured a divorce. She had been somewhat of a bomboy in her girlhood and some of the characteristics remained. These amused me. Her generosity and liberalism made me grow very much in love with her. This was one of the motives behind the suicide attempt.

We've covered most of the territory by verbal conversation so I don't see any use repeating it, Doctor.

As for dreams, here's the best I can remember. Naturally when I was planning escape at Farview, I used to dream about that. The only odd thing I can remember is that when I am falling in my dreams, I get an awful sickening feeling in the pit of the stomach. Several times I have dreamed of falling. Probably the phobia I have for falling, dates back to the time I fell down the stairs when I was sleep walking. I recall being truly frightened then. Heighth doesn't bother me when I'm conscious. That is, I can walk a steel beam at a high distance without it bothering me. I have no

Wright's pre-operative typing (a portion of his case history).

Post-operative memo.   **M**ayil 18, 1947
By Don Quixote   Montefiore Hosp.

A memo report is what is needed in this case. *t will determine if the

patient is still sick or is just putting it on. Maybe he's putting it on. Who

knows?   Life is a strange characteristic of charxcters.

Wright's typing on the third post-operative day.

LESSON FOUR

Lesson four constitutes an inanity in itself.   I have a str nge feeling
to commit theft onde again if the opportuhity occurrs. Do you believe it will occur? I'm
not sure but I should like to know for reasons of my awn. Well, let's look at the case as
it stands now. Here John is. Working very day nd I'm not sure that he'll do what he
can to stop the necessary movem-nts that are coming up in the near future. What do you think
of this set-up, dear? Do you think it will work as well as we felt it might? Let's look
at the standing gear and see whet it has to offver before we goany further in our investiga-
tions. What is yo r opinion? Let's look into the furnace und see if the coals are still
warm yet? It might be worth our trouble anyway. I'm not cuite sure that all things does
dus rightly. Are you? Well, we're here so let's stay for the night.   A'm only running
off the mouth and we'll see what can be done to ehlp the countryside for many days to dome.
There are many poeple interested in this crisis. I think it w ll be to our advanture to
try to aid the countryside before it get too late, John. Anyhow let's look into the dimeter
and see what it has to offer before we proceed anyfuther, my dear?   Lots of things can
happen to us if we aren't careful. The point is to find out what has occurred to Jo n, first.
After this checking we can then check with with the overbrook co and see what can be said
for the people living there. How's that stand up to your ideas of wonderful adtantage? I'l
not sure that'll work, my dear. But we'll try before it get too late to do the things that
Joe requests us to do.

        Well, we'll bring this message to a close so that leave you not without a pur-
pose in life. life. life life life life life life life life life life life life life life,
life, life, life, life, life, life, life, l fe , life k, life, life, life, life, life, life,
life, life, life, lkife life, life, life, life, life, life, life, life, life, life, life, life,
life, life, life, life, life, life, life, life, life, life, life, life, life, life, life, life,
life, life, life, life, life, life, life, life, life, life, life, life, life, life, life, life,
life, life, life, life, life, life, life, life, life,, life, life, life, life, life, life, life,
 life, life, life, life. life, life, life, life, life, life, life life, life, life, life, life

life, life, life, life, life, life, life, life life, life, life, life, life, life, l

Wright's typing on the ninth post-operative day.

POSTOPERATIVE REPORT
Lesson 25

Since it's only going to be a relatively short time till I'm on the
"bricks", I'll write and tell Miss Stuckey that I'll call on her myself. That
will settle the question and elimiinate complications. There can be nothing
important that she wishes to see me about except a girl's whim. So we can let
the matter ride temporarily. Ok? She had written me asking to visit me. I
ask the deputies and they passed the buck to you so I told her to get in touch
with you. That is how it came about.

Before I forget it, Doctor, I want to thank you wholeheartedly for your
past, compassionate consideration of my whims. It wasn't a case of just nursing me along because of my tyranical attitude or spoiled appetites, it was a case
of "nursing" me along because they reasons which I presented were very real to
me. After all every human has valuations that he places a price upon and insists
that the other party meet these responsibilities. It wasn't a case of me being
a confirmed malingerer or a hypo, it was a case of me driving for an insurance
policy for protection, because as a layman, Doctor, I knew very little about
brain surgery, therefore I tried to get the best insurance policy I could for
self-preservation. Please try to understand a layman's point of view. An operation of the type performed was "duck soup" to you because you had done so many
before, but to me it was something along the "unknown" and I was naturally
worried. Can't blame me. Any person would worry. Even one-armed Pat took the
thing very serious. He had to have some moral support. We did what we could to
give it to him. He's a pathetic soul and needs some help. I do pray the operation is a success in his case. I'm quite confident it will be. That's how
faith I have in you.

Wright's typing, illustrating return to pre-operative level.

ABOUT THE AUTHORS

YALE DAVID KOSKOFF, Chief of the Department of Neurosurgery at Montefiore Hospital in Pittsburgh, was born in New Haven, Connecticut, in 1905. In 1926 he was graduated from Yale College, later from its medical school, where he taught neurophysiology. He received his training in neurosurgery at Boston City Hospital and Lahey Clinic.

RICHARD GOLDHURST was the Associate Editor of the *Carolina Israelite* for ten years. He has published a novel, *The Deceivers*, now in its third edition.